# AMERICA'S NEW POLICY MAKERS
## The Scientists' Rise to Power

## Other Books by the Author

Spacepower *
Rocketry Through the Ages *
Man in the Universe *
Stations in Space
The Space Race

* With Michael Stoiko

# AMERICA'S NEW POLICY MAKERS
# The Scientists' Rise to Power

## Donald W. Cox

## CHILTON BOOKS

A DIVISION OF CHILTON COMPANY

*Publishers*

Philadelphia and New York

# To

All those scientists who performed so well in Act I of "The Age of Space," and who—it is sincerely hoped—will play an even more significant role in Act II of this drama so that we all may live to see Act III

# Acknowledgments

To all those scientists whom I interviewed and with whom I corresponded during the research phase of this project, I am extremely grateful. Most of their names appear in the last section of the Bibliography, so I shall not repeat them here. Two nonscientists must be singled out for their sincere and untiring devotion in helping to prepare the manuscript for the publisher: Diane Dulaney, for her constructive editorial criticisms in smoothing out the rough spots in my writing style, and Roseann Timony, for her translation of my original hieroglyphics into a clean, typed, final form.

My appreciation also goes to those publishers and authors who have kindly given me permission to extract short quotations from their works which have enhanced my efforts: *Government and Science,* Don K. Price, New York University Press; *Now It Can Be Told,* Leslie R. Groves, Harper and Row; *American Scientists and Nuclear Weapon Policy,* Robert Gilpin, Princeton University Press; *The Two Cultures and the Scientific Revolution,* C. P. Snow, Cambridge University Press; *Social Theory and Social Structure,* Robert K. Merton, Free Press; and *Nationalism in Politics,* Michael Oakeshott, Basic Books.

Lastly, to my loving wife, Jane, for her patient and quiet support during the six-month incubation period of this work, and to Ed Reddoch for giving me the original idea for the book.

DONALD W. COX

# Preface

For any citizen aware of the increasingly momentous interplay between American science and politics, the dearth of either popular or academic books on the subject comes as a painful discovery. The few recent books written by political scientists and historians are devoted to limited aspects of the complex relationships between Government and science.

Since Sputnik I there has been a healthy proliferation of speeches and articles by responsible scientists on individual aspects of Government-science relations, but, as yet, few books have come from these men of science. The big picture—in perspective—was skillfully presented by Dr. Don K. Price, dean of the Harvard Graduate School of Public Administration, in *Government and Science*. The publication date of this volume, however, is 1954, three years before the dramatic event that startled Americans on October 4, 1957. Almost a decade has gone by without a comprehensive discussion in print of the expanding role of the American scientist in our political system.

Neither has there been an attempt, as far as this writer has been able to determine, to present a popular history of the rise of American science in Government from its humble beginnings to the present. For these reasons, I have undertaken this work in the hope that it will fill a gulf in the public's need to know, until the academic historians, who are still struggling to unravel the mass of valuable scientific material accumulated during World War II years, can catch up.

vii

In a work emphasizing contemporary events, it is impossible to cover adequately all aspects of the phenomenal rise of science in Government circles. I have had, therefore, to be selective, and I have eliminated the detailed story of the scientific and political controversies over the worth of our fallout shelter program, our overkill capacities, fail-safe devices, and the war games theories. I have purposely underplayed the role of the atomic scientists—important figures in the recent technological-political developments on the world stage—because their story has been told before.

Rather, I have concentrated on the rise to influence of the newer group of space scientists. While narrating from this specific viewpoint, I have not neglected to point out the growing interrelationships, not always apparent, between the atomic scientists and their colleagues, the space scientists, since both these groups will play an increasingly significant role in the ultimate determination of our nation's destiny.

I have arbitrarily divided my analysis into two parts. Part I presents a history of the relationship of science to Government from the origins of our nation to the present attempts at Geneva to achieve a nuclear test ban. Part II is an analysis of the unsolved problems stemming from the invasion of the political arena by the scientists.

Many conflicting opinions surround such pressing questions as: Should the scientists in Government be restricted to advisory roles only? Or should they make policy too? Should they run for political office? Should we have a Department of Science at the Cabinet level? How can we best achieve a national science policy? What about the growing restrictions on scientific freedom? How can the scientists express their concern for the survival of humanity in a more effective way?

These—and other—topics are discussed here, with the hope that the reader will leave these pages a bit more enlightened about a subject that directly affects his everyday life—both now and tomorrow.

DONALD W. COX

# Introduction

Throughout man's history, the inventions of science and technology have had a disrupting effect on the established social order.

The ever-widening stream of technical progress has led to a greater influence of science on our whole fabric of civilization, from the top rungs of Government down to the daily life of the individual citizen. To make the necessary adjustments we need trained scientists to help our politicians and Government administrators leap over the hurdles that would separate us from the best utilization of scientific advances.

Sir Charles P. Snow, a prominent British scientist-novelist, recently called his fellow scientists the "most important occupational group in the world today," because what they do is of passionate concern to the whole of human society. While admitting that, as a group, scientists have had little part in the world's decisions on how the products of their minds and laboratories are to be utilized, he stressed that ". . . potentially, they can have a great influence." Snow felt that the rest of the world was frightened by the scientists and tended to think them radically different from other men.

"Whether they [the scientists] like it or not," Snow told an audience of American scientists, "what they do is of critical importance for the human race. Intellectually, it has transformed the climate of our time. Socially, it will decide whether we live or die, and how we live or die. It holds decisive powers for good and evil. That is the situation in which the scientists find themselves. They may not have asked for it, or only have asked for it in part, but they cannot escape it. They think, many of the more sensitive of them, that they don't deserve to have this weight of responsibility heaved upon them. All they want to do is to get on with their work. I sympathize. *But the scientists can't escape the responsibility—any more than they, or the rest of us, can escape the gravity of the moment in which we stand.*" [Author's italics.]

In this era of rapid transition to a highly technical society, the many challenges presented both to the scientists and to society itself are enormous. The accelerated rate of introduction of new technical processes, coupled with the exploding birth

ix

rate, finds our nation calling for help to the very creators of the mechanical wonders which can either destroy or save us. These men, once content to work quietly inside their laboratories, have been pulled into the very center of political life because they let the genie escape from the test tubes to create a monumental disorder in society. This maladjustment pervades our entire society from the highest levels of diplomacy and military planning to the job retraining of individuals who have been automated out of work.

The scientific approach to policy making is described by the statement of the noted British astronomer, Dr. Fred Hoyle: "Policies [theories] of science are to be judged by their results, and by their results alone." In the past, the subject matter of scientific judgments has been of little emotional significance to the peoples of the world. But when we discuss scientific policies on such issues as mutual thermonuclear suicide, fallout shelters, the high cost of landing a man on the moon, and the right to conduct atomic tests in the atmosphere, then we have entered the realm of politics, and all hopes of rendering a decision based purely on the unemotional rationale of the scientific approach are soon lost.

Just because the human factor has entered the picture does not mean that the scientific approach to policy making has failed and should be consigned to the graveyard of history. Rather, we must seek new means of adapting the scientific approach to this new state of affairs.

Dr. Harrison Brown, a distinguished University of California scientist, has defined the situation: "As our industrial society becomes increasingly complex, as our supplies of high-grade reserves decrease, as our population increases and as military technological developments accelerate, our dependence upon science and technology will continue to increase. More and more we will find scientific and technological considerations entering into government decision-making processes. Every government agency will be affected, ranging from State and Defense to Commerce, Interior and Agriculture. . . ."

In view of this rapidly growing dependence, it is important that we ask ourselves a number of questions. Is there adequate recognition of this problem in the legislative and executive branches of Government and in political circles generally? How can governmental problems involving science and technology be handled adequately within the framework of democratic processes? Is the scientific community at large prepared to accept the increasing governmental responsibilities which probably will be thrust upon it? How will scientists act in times of crises?

Prompt and comprehensive answers to these questions are important for our nation's welfare. Already, in some cases, we discover that scientists are no longer acting simply in an advisory capacity but are exercising *policy-making* powers in key Government posts. This subtle change has been taking place right under our eyes ever since Sputnik and has radically altered the traditional concept of the scientist in Government.

This problem of delineating the fuzzy line between advising and policy making is only one of the myriad obstacles that have arisen in recent times to plague our scientists and Government officials. Ever since Alamagordo and Sputnik, American scientists have viewed with growing concern the troublesome problems arising from the interaction between rapid scientific progress and public affairs. With each new scientific advance, a corresponding increase in social power ensues, making more complex the problem of directing its use for beneficial ends. If the right decisions are not promptly made, the consequences can be disastrous—as the threat of nuclear war over Cuba in 1962 proved.

Our scientists themselves have recognized that we are in the midst of the most profound scientific revolution in the history of man, where the forces now being brought under human control are matching the power and immensity of nature itself.

As early as 1956 a committee of the American Association for the Advancement of Science realized the crisis that had arisen from science's inability to achieve its appropriate place in the decisive political, economic, and social processes which were daily becoming more dependent on scientific achievements for the resolution of social issues.

Dr. Alvin Weinberg of Oak Ridge, recently commenting on this point, said: "Nuclear energy, along with other modern technologies, has made obsolete the traditional geographic, political and economic fragmentation of the world." He was not alone in his observations, since the late Dr. John von Neumann, who originated our ICBM program, pointed out more than a decade ago that the intercontinental ballistics rocket had made geographic boundaries obsolete.

Nuclear energy is not the only area of modern technology that is leading the way toward unification of the world. "Our communications systems, our transportation systems . . . all of these and many other new technologies point strongly to the mismatch between the size of our political and economic units and the size of our technology," said Weinberg.

Scientists and nonscientists alike hope that, before these new instruments destroy us, our political instruments will adjust themselves so that the great fruits of these new scientific break-throughs can be used to benefit man in a peaceful world.

Another hidden contemporary problem of the scientists in Government was aired by Supreme Court Justice William O. Douglas, who wrote in a recently published pamphlet, *Freedom of the Mind:* "New centers of power are in the hands of those who control science, and one who traces the controls back to origins often finds the Pentagon in the central position. Those who finance the scientific revolution usually control those who work for them. The impact of this control on our universities is so great that their autonomy is threatened."

Despite these unanswered problems, there is a greater liaison between scientists and the Government today than ever before in our history. The $15 billion of public tax money expended for scientific research in 1963 alone is living proof that the scientist is over his neck in politics. For, wherever public money flows in such great abundance, politics follows close behind. It is up to the concerned citizen, acting as a marriage counselor, to see that the two partners—Government and science—keep their marriage harmonious. If the marriage should ever founder, then our nation's destiny will be profoundly and sadly affected. But, in one sense, these two partners can never really be divorced, even if they wish. They are linked together by a bond of comradeship. Only you, the reader, and the course of history, can determine their real strength.

DONALD W. COX

*Philadelphia, Pa.*
*September, 1963*

# Contents

xiv  *Contents*

# AMERICA'S NEW POLICY MAKERS
## The Scientists' Rise to Power

In holding scientific research and discovery in respect, as we should, we must be alert to the equal and opposite danger that public policy could itself become the captive of a scientific-technological elite.

—*President Dwight D. Eisenhower*
Farewell Address

Washington, D.C.
January 18, 1961

# PART I

## The Expanding Role of Science in Government

Throughout history, societies have expressed their aspirations in large scale, monumental enterprises. . . . The Pyramids . . . symbolize Egypt; the magnificent cathedrals symbolize church culture of the Middle Ages; Versailles symbolizes the France of Louis XIV.

When history looks at the twentieth century, she will . . . find in the monuments of Big Science—the huge rockets, the high-energy accelerators, the high-flux research reactors—symbols of our time.

—*Dr. Alvin Weinberg,*
Director of the Oak Ridge National
Laboratory, 1962

# Chapter 1

# From Boiler Explosions to Einstein
# 1790-1940

Science played no part in the life of the early settlers of colonial America. Rather, the economy of the tiny British colonies was based on maritime trade—in molasses, rum, and slaves —fishing, and trapping. Our Founding Fathers, fortunately, did have a preliminary vision of the importance of science to the growth of the new nation. Quietly, they sowed the seeds of scientific interest and endeavor which were to transform the weak infant nation into a lusty, brawling young giant within a century and a half through the adaptation of the technological wonders of the Industrial Revolution.

George Washington was a surveyor and engineer by profession. He ardently sought the establishment of a national university to serve as a center for the advancement of the sciences. Benjamin Franklin was the most distinguished scientist, inventor, and experimenter in colonial America. Thomas Jefferson was noted for his wide range of scientific interests. Alexander Hamilton advocated a system of bounties and subsidies to scientists and inventors as a critical part of his program for the stimulation and development of manufacturing in the young nation.

Overriding the objections of those who advocated limited central Government, under President Washington the nation gave increasing Government status to science. Federal assistance began modestly in 1790 with the creation of the Patent Office, the inauguration of the decennial census, and the development of a uniform system of weights and measures.

Many of the scientific activities in which the Government now engages were initiated in the nineteenth century. Federal action took three major interrelated forms during the past century: protection and support for science and technology, use of science and technology to accomplish governmental purposes, and cooperation with the growing number of scientific and technological societies.

In 1832, the first governmental grant for experimental research was made by the United States Treasury Department to the Franklin Institute in Philadelphia for an investigation of steam boiler explosions in steamboats. Research at the Institute (America's first nonprofit research organization) led to the establishment in 1837 of the nation's first Federal regulatory agency: the Steamboat Inspection Service. Shortly thereafter, the first national railroad regulations were written into law— as a result of the Institute's demonstration that many railroad disasters could have been avoided through a uniform code of railway signals. These were only the first of scores of Federal agencies set up following recommendations of our scientists.

It was agriculture, however, which received a major portion of the Government's scientific attention in the early years of the Republic, since farming most directly affected the national welfare. Washington had proposed a national board of agriculture but he was blocked by Jefferson's strict interpretation of the Constitution. Yet Jefferson encouraged the development of state and local agricultural societies and their nation-wide cooperation. As a result of the efforts of these local societies, and of the young American Association for the Advancement of Science, agricultural experimental stations sprang up independently.

In 1851, the president of the A.A.A.S. argued: "There are few applications of Science that do not bear on the interests of commerce and navigation, naval or military concerns, the customs, the lighthouses, the public lands, post offices and postroads, either directly or remotely." The strong early impact of science on the American government was further enhanced through close early cooperation between scientists and Government officials.

With the establishment of the Department of Agriculture and the passage of the Morrill Act in 1862, the pace of the Government's intervention and interest in science quickened. Beginning with experimentation in the agricultural sciences (which had begun quietly in 1836 when the Commissioner of Patents began to distribute free seeds to farmers), the Department then moved into research in economics, statistics, and other fields. This comprehensive agricultural program set a basic pattern for later Federal action in scientific technological fields.

The Morrill Act, following the precedent of the Northwest Ordinance of 1787, established our land-grant colleges and set in motion a vast Federal-state cooperative system of education and research. By the end of the nineteenth century, agricultural experiment stations were associated with the colleges and the Government in Washington started to make substantial cash grants to the states for agricultural research. As the Department of Agriculture grew in stature, it was able to weld these stations into the first nation-wide research facility directed to the service of public needs.

Although agriculture was the first, it was not the exclusive object of Federal scientific interest. As the country grew, surveying and mapping became essential, and the Government supported this scientific task. In the years before the Civil War, the Government's principal scientific activities were the underwriting of the Lewis and Clark Expedition to the Northwest and the setting up of the Army's Department of Topographical Engineers. The Coastal Survey was established in 1807, followed by the founding of the nation's first engineering school at West Point.

The observation and the collection of data about natural phenomena led to the early establishment of the Naval Observatory. All of these agencies were kept busy accumulating information to aid the young nation's commerce, defense, and westward expansion.

Another area of Government involvement in science began in a most peculiar manner. At his death in 1829, English chemist James Smithson, a bachelor, left a strange will, bequeathing his fortune to his nephew, with the stipulation that the estate should pass on to the nephew's heirs. If the nephew were to have no heirs, Smithson made a gamble. He wrote, "I then bequest the whole of my property . . . to the United States of America, to be founded at Washington, an establishment for the increase and diffusion of knowledge among men."

Fortunately for our country, his nephew also died without heirs in 1838. On December 6, 1838, the U.S. Congress received formal advice of this peculiar windfall's arrival in a Message of State from President Martin Van Buren. Smithson's fortune was in gold—half a million old-fashioned dollars' worth. Unfortunately, Congress was preoccupied with the financial panic of 1837 and the deep-rooted domestic wrangle over states' rights *vs.* a strong Federal government. A proposal for a national bank had just been defeated, for the bank had been seen as a threat of overpowering centralization. To many politicians of the day, an "establishment" owned by the United States and charged with the "increase and diffusion of knowledge among men" could mean only one thing: a national university. Therefore, wouldn't such a new creation encompass the same acceptance of the Federalist principle rejected in the debate over the national bank?

Congress wrangled for eight years over the issue, while Smithson's gold that had been "wisely" invested in canal bonds for "safe keeping" depreciated scandalously. Finally, 17 years after Smithson's death, Congress quashed a last-ditch move by the states' rights' advocates to return the bequest to England. In 1846, President James Polk signed a law authorizing the establishment of the Smithsonian Institution as our first national science foundation. Since science was now enjoying popular prestige, following the invention of the telegraph and the steam locomotive, Congress set up a board of distinguished regents which included three U.S. Senators, three Congressmen, the Chief Justice of the Supreme Court, and the Vice-President of the United States. Chosen as the Smithsonian's first secretary was the brilliant young physicist Joseph Henry, who discovered the principles of electromagnetism which formed the basis of Samuel F. B. Morse's patent for the telegraph.

The group of distinguished scientists selected to compose this quasi-Government organization, the Smithsonian, became a self-perpetuating body directed by law to study and support "any subject of science or art" when called upon by a Government department. While several new technical devices came into use during the great War Between the States, relatively few civilian scientists undertook any work on military equipment or weapons. Institute Secretary Henry, however, believed in the feasibility of the "lighthouses of the sky" first proposed by John Quincy Adams. Although the taunts of his political opponents almost ruined his reputation, Henry supported the historic Yankee balloon experiment of the Civil War. These bulbous military "lighthouses" added a third dimension to the battlefield and helped influence Lincoln to foster the chartering of the National Academy of Sciences in 1863.

Henry, as the first scientist to not only advise but to actually *make policy* within the Federal government, initiated and organized the first effort to chart happenings outside the earth's atmosphere by methodically recording changes in the daily weather.

In the last half of the nineteenth century, there was a steady growth in the Government's scientific effort, characterized by an expansion of its data-gathering service undertaken in the public interest. The growth of the Coast and Geodetic Survey, the Weather Bureau, and the Census Bureau marked this period. Reconstruction saw the establishment of more scientific bodies designed to carry out new responsibilities of the Government: the Medical and Signal Corps of the Army, the testing and soil analysis branch of the Department of Agriculture, and the National Bureau of Standards. The National Academy of Sciences called upon these various data- and material-gathering agencies often in the years that followed the Civil War.

The patterns set in the nineteenth century were expanded in

the twentieth. The National Bureau of Standards was finally established in 1901 after many years of lobbying by the National Academy. The Department of Commerce and Labor, established in 1903, began scientific research on problems of industry and labor. The findings provided the basis for later Government activity in these areas and led to the division of the department into today's separate Department of Commerce and Department of Labor.

Private foundations soon sprang to the support of science in all fields, and, in some cases, began directing their scientists' attention to problems of particular governmental interest. Don K. Price, in his book *Government and Science,* summarized this record when he wrote: "The federal government after starting with a theory that denied the traditional doctrines of sovereignty, gradually built up its powers and functions to make use of the applied sciences for the development of the new continent, and ultimately to meet the needs of an industrialized economy. In this process, the national associations and organizations of scientists and their professional colleagues—working within their specialized groups without regard to partisan allegiance or to the boundaries between government and private life—supplied the most dynamic initiative."

This cooperative effort was probably best dramatized by the life of the American scientist whose invention was to have the greatest impact on the world during the latter part of the present century. For he got his first big push to success as a young man from the joint support of a Government science institution and a private foundation.

This was Dr. Robert Hutchings Goddard, an unassuming physics professor, who in 1908 started experimenting with liquid rocket fuels in the basement laboratories of the Worcester Polytechnic Institute in Massachusetts. Because the strangling billows of acrid fumes became so intense, the college authorities requested him to "stop playing with those infernal rockets." Moving on to Clark University, Goddard came up in 1912 with the mathematical calculations which persuaded him that a relatively small amount of fuel could carry a heavily loaded vehicle high into the sky if the rockets were properly built.

After four more years of experimenting, he found himself without funds, his only remaining resource being his laboratory at Clark. Although he lacked money-raising experience, he possessed a sincere earnestness and enthusiasm. So in 1916 he wrote down his big idea and mailed it to Charles D. Walcott, the visionary secretary of the Smithsonian in Washington. Walcott had already unwittingly engaged himself in the birth of space travel, through his support of Congress's establishment of the National Advisory Committee on Aeronautics the year before, in 1915.

Goddard mentioned in his prospectus to Walcott that it should be possible to fire a rocket that would reach the moon. And, he wrote, if the cargo were "13.82—or less—pounds of flash powder," the rocket's impact would be "strikingly visible" to observers on earth.

"This plan," the father of American rocketry wrote dryly, "although a matter of much general interest, is not of obvious scientific importance." But Walcott was impressed and immediately replied warmly with a query as to how much money Goddard needed. Walcott's response was so unexpectedly generous that the rocket enthusiast cut his requirements in half, asking for only $5,000. He received it, along with an additional $6,000 a short time afterward. So, with a picayune total of $11,000 of Smithsonian funds (and later some Guggenheim Foundation money), the science of modern rocketry was born.

Goddard's report to the Smithsonian concerning his experiments made its way to the libraries of Europe where Herman Oberth used it as the basis of his famous book, *The Rocket Into Interplanetary Space*. This volume, published in 1923, led to a whole chain of subsequent events from Von Braun to Peenemunde to Huntsville to Cape Canaveral and now to the moon.

During World War I, Thomas Alva Edison, the most respected American scientist of his time, was given the responsibility of mobilizing civilian science and technology for the war effort. He displayed a marked indifference to the growing need for technical guidance within our Government with his suggestion to the U.S. Navy that it should bring at least one physicist into the war effort in case it "became necessary to calculate something." If Edison were alive today, how shocked he would be by the presence of not one, but thousands of scientists working for the Government!

Immediately after the close of the war, the infant National Advisory Committee on Aeronautics began a research program that was destined to pave the way for the new commercial and military aircraft that were to make their appearance in the second quarter of this century.

During the latter stages of World War I, a new quasi-governmental agency, the National Research Council, was established by the National Academy of Sciences with the cooperation of the nation's scientific and technical societies to make the country's scientific resources more available to the Government.

In the period between the two world wars, Government science continued to expand in an orderly fashion. Various institutes of health were created as part of the Public Health Service, and Federal medical research began to grow rapidly. The War and Navy Departments built many new research facilities. Even the social scientists finally were recognized by the Government during this period. Several of them were hired by the Commerce, Labor and Agriculture Departments and began playing a quiet role in data collecting.

The great depression of the thirties resulted in extensive reconsideration of the relationship of science to politics. The eminent physiologist A. V. Hill said in 1933: "Science should remain aloof and detached, not from any sense of superiority, not from any indifference to the common welfare, but as a condition of complete intellectual honesty. Emotion, entirely necessary in ordinary life, is utterly out of place in making scientific decisions. If science is to continue to make progress, it must insist on keeping its traditional position of independence, it must refuse to meddle with, or to be dominated by, divinity, morals, politics or rhetoric."

Although some fellow scientists agreed with Hill in his isolationist ivory tower attitude, there was a growing tide of dissent from this view within scientific ranks. In later years, Hill himself altered his stand and even assumed a Government position for a short time.

As the thirties drew to a close, and the nation slowly pulled itself out of the depths of the depression and subsequent recession, we were not aware that in several European laboratories independent scientific experiments were taking place that were soon to shock the whole world. These European scientists were tearing away at the underpinnings of the accepted public knowledge of what science could and could not accomplish. The typical American scientist, whether working in a university, in industry, or for the Government, was also unaware of these rumblings from across the ocean.

The first revelation in the United States that the world of science was on the threshold of a momentous breakthrough came with the news of atom-splitting attempts by Niels Bohr in Denmark and Otto Hahn and Fritz Strassman in Berlin. The impact of this information was understood by only a small group of European refugee physicists, including Leo Szilard, Enrico Fermi, Edward Teller, and Eugene Wigner. Dr. Szilard took the initiative to pay a visit to Albert Einstein in mid-1939 to break the news to him.

Accompanied by Wigner, Szilard went to Princeton with the idea of trying to convince Einstein to persuade the Belgian government, through his old friend Queen Elizabeth of Belgium, to stop its uranium exports from the Belgian Congo to Germany. Szilard, a Hungarian, and Fermi, an Italian, had both previously failed in attempts to interest the U.S. Navy in conducting research work on uranium.

Szilard and Wigner were more successful in their visit with Einstein than they had hoped, and together the three decided that the white-thatched discoverer of the theory of relativity should write a letter to President Roosevelt. Several drafts of the letter were prepared during a period of two months before the final historic composition was delivered to the President in October, 1939, through an intermediary, Dr. Alex Sachs, an economist and unofficial adviser to the President.

In explaining the reason for his letter, Einstein wrote: "I am a convinced and dedicated man, but not an absolute pacifist." This change of position required courage of a rare sort, and helped to impress the President with the import of the letter's contents.

Roosevelt took immediate action, after digesting the contents of the Einstein letter, by appointing an advisory committee on uranium. But the basic idea behind the dramatic letter languished in America during the first year after its delivery. The Government allocated a mere $6,000 for uranium studies from November, 1939, to October 31, 1940. Although the Carnegie Institution contributed an additional $20,000 for atomic research, Sachs, Szilard, and Einstein had cause for great concern.

Time was running out. Would we be able to set up an atomic chain reaction before the Nazis and utilize its benefits for defense of the West? The small group of anxious scientists watched and worried—as the war in Europe threatened to engulf the whole world.

# Chapter 2

# Atomic Fallout from Alamagordo
# 1940-1946

Einstein's famous letter to FDR in the summer of 1939 marked the beginning of a new military, political, and socio-scientific era. American scientists were distressed that the order for "quick action," as urged by Einstein for our development of nuclear fission, was not forthcoming from the White House—while reports indicated that Germany was plunging far ahead of us in uranium research. Word trickled back that Hitler had halted the sale of uranium from the rich mines of Czecho-slovakia and stepped up the production of heavy water (used as a moderator in the reactors) at his captured refinery in Nor-way. This refinery was the only one of its type in the world in 1940.

Another cause for alarm was the report that leading physi-cists and nuclear experts from laboratories all over Germany had been brought together to concentrate on hitching the atom to Hitler's Juggernaut. The American scientists most alarmed by these reports were those who knew that a single pound of uranium-235 contained as much energy as 10,000 tons of TNT and a potential explosive pressure a million times greater.

Fortunately for the West, the German scientists dropped their project after deciding that producing an atomic bomb in time to put it to effective use for the Fatherland was an impossibility. We in America, on the other hand, waited until the day before Pearl Harbor to start our Manhattan Project and then spent $2 billion trying to catch up with Hitler in a race he had already abandoned.

A year later, on December 2, 1942, Enrico Fermi and his fellow scientists achieved the first critical atomic pile chain reaction at Stagg Field in Chicago. The atomic age was born, although the world had to wait two and a half more years for the dramatic post-birth pangs of Alamagordo, Hiroshima, and Nagasaki.

Meanwhile, America was gearing herself to fight a global war for the first time in her history. Several new organizations were established to carry out the great bulk of our military research. The Office of Scientific Research and Development was set up under Dr. Vannevar Bush of M.I.T., who became the leading wartime figure in meeting military problems with scientific analysis. Science had now taken a new place, not merely as a tool for social benefit but as a major weapon of war.

The chief Government agencies involved were the OSRD, through its two major constituents, the National Defense Research Council and the Committee for Medical Research, the Manhattan Engineering District, and the War Department's Corps of Engineers (which took over the supervision of nuclear fission begun by the National Defense Research Council). Each of these entities leaned heavily on Government contracts, primarily with the physics research divisions of many of our leading universities, for the actual carrying out of their programs.

The Manhattan District, under the command of General Leslie R. Groves, recruited scientists who worked in secrecy at Chicago, Los Alamos, New Mexico, Oak Ridge, Tennessee, and Hanford, Washington, to develop the bomb. Groves felt that the scientists under him were unruly fellows who did not want to live under proper discipline. In his memoirs, *Now It Can Be Told: The Story of the Manhattan Project,* Groves stated that they always wanted to break down the walls of compartmentalization and thus break security. This tendency on their part led to the so-called colloquium at Los Alamos, where the scientists exchanged bits of information to maintain morale and achieve a feeling of common purpose and responsibility. "From the standpoint of security," wrote Groves, "it presented a major hazard and it was one of the reasons why the treachery of [Klaus] Fuchs was so disastrous for the free world."

Actually, the project succeeded in a short time *because* the compartments broke down, although Groves never admitted—or realized—this. As one Los Alamos scientist put it: "In this place, you can succeed only if you manage to find out what you are NOT SUPPOSED TO KNOW."

As early as September 30, 1944, many months before the first atomic device was tested and before the Manhattan District officials were even sure it would work, two distinguished American scientists, James B. Conant, president of Harvard, and Vannevar Bush, president of the Carnegie Institution in Washington, warned Secretary of War Henry L. Stimson of future "super-super" bombs that could be delivered by guided missiles. They also urged that America demonstrate the bomb first before actually using it against Japan, either "over enemy territory, or in our own country" with subsequent notice that it would be used against the enemy's "mainland unless surrender was forthcoming."

After the nuclear scientists brought the atomic bomb project to a successful completion in 1944, they had time to ponder the political and moral consequences of man's taming of atomic energy. Some of the scientists felt it was their duty to bring to the attention of the nation the immensity and urgency of the problems that would follow military victory. Under the leadership of James Franck, the self-appointed "Committee on Social and Political Implications," whose members included Glenn T. Seaborg, Leo Szilard, and Eugene Rabinowitch, drew up a petition which was completed and delivered to the President in June, 1945. The committee argued that the primary political-military aim of the United States in the postwar years should be the prevention of an atomic arms race and that the only means of avoiding such a race would be the international control of atomic energy.

The report, named for committee chairman Franck, recommended to Secretary of War Stimson that the atomic bomb first be used on a barren or desert island, since the scientists feared the military and political implications of using the weapon on a military target. The Franck Report concluded: "One thing is clear. Any international agreement on prevention of nuclear armaments must be backed by actual and efficient controls. No paper agreement can be sufficient since neither this nor any other nation can stake its whole existence on trust in other nations' signatures." Unfortunately, it was upon this shoal of "actual and efficient controls" that the Baruch plan for the peaceful control of atomic energy foundered a few years later.

After receipt of the Franck Report, four of the other senior scientists—Enrico Fermi, J. Robert Oppenheimer, Arthur Compton, and E. O. Lawrence—who worked on the bomb were called in to advise Stimson's Interim Committee. The scientists were charged to advise the Secretary of War on the postwar uses of atomic energy and to study alternative uses of the first atomic bombs—in a demonstration *vs.* actual use in the war. After spending a long, agonizing week end at Los Alamos on June 9–10, 1945, they rejected the conclusions of the Franck Report. These scientists were mindful, as the Franck committee was not, that our arsenal would initially have only two combat nuclear weapons. It was vitally important that they be used to persuade the Japanese to surrender. Returning to Washington, the panel of four scientists informed Secretary Stimson that it could "propose no technical demonstration likely to bring an end to the war."

Their recommendations were seconded by General Groves, who rejected both the Franck Report and the results of a secret poll taken by several scientists during mid-July in the aftermath of the Alamagordo test success, urging that the bomb *not* be used on a live city target. Although Bush, Conant, and Lawrence were visibly upset after Alamagordo, Groves "thought they were now completely wrapped up with the preparations for the coming climax in Japan."

In a last desperate attempt to prevent the unrestricted use

of the A-bomb on Japan without warning, Szilard addressed—
in ink—a bundle of petitions to "The President of the United
States." Upon receiving the sealed brown manila envelope from
Chicago, Colonel Kenneth D. Nichols, production chief of the
Manhattan Project, sent it by special messenger on July 25th
from Oak Ridge to Washington. He urged that "these papers
be forwarded to the President of the United States with proper
comments." The various petitions which were relayed through
General Groves included Szilard's, signed by 70 scientists; another by 18 Chicago scientists; a document signed by 68 scientists at Oak Ridge; and a poll of 150 scientists in Chicago.
Most of the signatories strongly opposed the dropping of the
bomb without warning.

Since President Truman was then in Potsdam at a conference
with Stalin and Churchill, Groves decided to hold the bundle
of petitions until August 1st. Then he had them sent over to
Stimson's office, just as Truman was about to embark for home
aboard the *Augusta*. These papers—which might have changed
the course of history—never reached the President in time, as
the bomb was dropped while he was still aboard the warship
in the Atlantic. Unknown to the scientists, Secretary Stimson
had approved final orders on July 25th to drop an A-bomb
on Japan without warning "after about 3 August 1945."

President Truman looked upon the question of dropping the
A-bomb as solely a "military decision." Relying on the counsel
of his Secretary of War and the four members of the Scientific
Advisory Panel—Fermi, Lawrence, Oppenheimer, and Compton—made it possible for him to disregard the moral issues by
declaring that this novel type of warfare was ethically admissible.
The cold compulsion that hovered over the deliberations as to
the use of the bomb, despite the initial peace overtures of the
beaten enemy, helped to force the issue. The "scientific" experiment had to be made, and even Einstein, godfather of the Manhattan Project, felt "completely powerless to prevent the fateful decision." The builders of the bomb were no longer guardi-
ans of mankind and prophets of a new philosophy. They were,

after all, mortal men carried away with the pride and prejudices of their new technological accomplishment.

Overruling the desires of the scientists who had proposed that the bomb be preferably used in a demonstration on some uninhabited island, Groves proposed to Secretary Stimson that Hiroshima and Kyoto be the targets instead. The general could think only of the Americans who had lost their lives in the infamous Bataan Death March. Decisions were made quickly now, and on August 6, 1945, the destruction of Hiroshima was announced to a tense and war-weary world. To the scientists scattered throughout the Manhattan District the day was one of anguish, indignation, and remorse.

Although the dramatic harnessing of the atom focused public attention on the scientists working in the Manhattan District, many people forgot that other scientists had been working in less spectacular roles in other branches of the Government to help win the war.

Out of this proof of "man's inhumanity to man" the Federation of Atomic Scientists was born in late 1945 to give men of science a voice in public affairs. The Federation started out as a defensive organization, warding off the worst consequences of anti-science. Less formal groups like the sponsors and subscribers to the newborn *Bulletin of Atomic Scientists* took the added view that scientists could serve a useful function by proposing solutions to international political problems through the use of applied science. The *Bulletin* was started as a monthly voice to "encourage the study of the role of nuclear science in modern society and to gather and disseminate scientific information . . . and their impact on public affairs." Dr. Eugene Rabinowitch, who had worked with Fermi on the original atomic pile in Chicago, became the first editor and has remained at the helm ever since.

The publication began as a four-page newsletter circulated among several hundred scientists. (Today the *Bulletin* has international renown and a subscription list of 25,000.) The editors believe peace can best be achieved through a vigorous expression of the intricate interrelationship of science and the Government. The authors of *Bulletin* articles are also concerned with the positive applications of science to human welfare.

The Federation of Atomic Scientists and the *Bulletin* (which is published by the Educational Foundation for Nuclear Science, an independent subsidiary of the former group) unknowingly became a political lobbying instrument to push for both *civilian* and *international* control of the atom. Since they were neophytes in politics, most of the scientists did not realize that they were actually stepping beyond the borders of pure scientific advice in their testimony over various aspects of the control problem.

The mobilization of our whole society for winning a global war had made the Government the primary utilizer of scientific talent. Every type of scientist—from chemists to sociologists—had become quietly involved in the service of the country during the four years of conflict.

New accelerated patterns of the Federal government's scientific interest set during World War II would not be easily changed. The Office of Scientific Research and Development had demonstrated what could be accomplished through the rapid mobilization of our technical resources. The necessity of the initial secrecy and maintenance of Government monopoly in the infant atomic energy program guaranteed an extensive future Federal involvement in this new field of science. Other, less spectacular technological wartime achievements in radar and the proximity fuse helped to establish the pattern for later Government auspices of and involvement in postwar research and development.

As World War II drew to a sudden close, it became evident that our Government must continue to carry a major sustained responsibility for science. Continuing military needs demanded constant Government direction and stimulation in the growing complexities of military technology. No longer could we afford to return to the days of our prewar dependence on basic science leadership coming from outside the United States. Our economy was now dependent on advances in technology and it was up to the Government to ensure that these needs were met.

Although many citizens expressed concern about political interference and the dangers of centralizing authority in the Federal government for the expenditure of increasing amounts of money for research, development, and scientific education, no one argued for a return to the prewar situation of "science as usual." The question now had taken on a new complexion: *how much* would the government become involved in science in the future, and in *what* direction?

The immediate postwar period was a critical time for American scientists. Their popular acceptance and prestige were at an all-time high, but three important problems had to be resolved without delay: the adjustment of scientists to a peacetime world; the Pentagon's reorganization of science; and the control of the atom. Many of the scientists who had been working on wartime projects were eager to return to their university campuses. Although the Office of Scientific Research and Development was disbanded in 1945, national security required a continuation of some of the old projects into the postwar period. So, the military departments faced the problem of maintaining a core of their scientific facilities and personnel. Obviously, not all of the scientists were going to have their wishes fulfilled.

By late 1945, it was widely recognized that our basic research into new scientific knowledge had suffered greatly during the war. It was felt that our Government now had an obligation to support basic research. Key Government officials and scientists reiterated this need in their appearances before various Congressional committees in the months that followed V-J Day.

The transfer of the OSRD projects to the Department of Defense was accomplished in fairly smooth fashion. For example, the Air Force integrated the personnel and equipment of the M.I.T. Radiation Laboratory into its Cambridge Research Center. But getting enough money to conduct basic peacetime research was more difficult. At the request of President Roosevelt, Dr. Vannevar Bush had submitted a report early in 1945 on the steps needed to continue the nation's scientific advance.

In this widely publicized report, "Science, the Endless Frontier," the wartime head of the OSRD proposed the establishment of the National Research Foundation to support research and education in science and to disseminate scientific information. His advice was not heeded.

Meanwhile, through its new Office of Research and Inventions set up in 1945, the Navy Department became the principal source of Federal support for basic research in the years immediately following World War II. In 1946, by Act of Congress, it became the Office of Naval Research, expanding its activities to support basic research in many diverse scientific fields—of interest to the Navy. The National Institute of Health also supported this endeavor.

In June, 1946, the Secretaries of War and Navy established a Joint Research and Development Board to take the place of the disbanded OSRD. The new board was composed of Dr. Bush and representatives of each department. This committee of five was purely an interim arrangement for the study of military-scientific research and development and for the achievement of an agreement between the two departments on common policies and the allocation of responsibilities.

The Army tried to follow the Navy by setting up an Office of Army Research in the same year, 1946, but conservative generals aborted the effort. Not until six years later was this branch to establish a Chief of Research and Development (R&D) in the Office of the Chief of Staff. The Air Force was the last of the service departments to establish scientific positions of responsibility at the level of Assistant Secretary.

In addition to these changes, each of the military departments took a cue from the wartime OSRD and set up three separate contractor-operated scientific R&D centers. The Army established an Operations Research Office at Johns Hopkins; the Navy set up an Operations Evaluation Group at M.I.T.; and the Air Force, not to be outdone, established their supersecret, nonprofit research outfit called the RAND Corporation. (RAND stood for R&D, naturally.) Within a decade after the war, two dozen scientific research centers had sprung up in the U.S.—all working for the military.

The third—and most significant—postwar national science problem concerned the question of who was going to control the atom. General Groves wanted the military, through the Army, to continue to maintain jurisdiction over the development of the atom after the war was over. He was both disappointed and bitter when Secretary of State James F. Byrnes appointed a special State Department Committee composed of Dean Acheson, John J. McCloy, Vannevar Bush, James Conant, and himself to recommend a postwar atomic program. Groves wanted to run the show himself, with only the two scientists as advisers, but he was outvoted.

He also discovered to his dismay that a new panel headed by David Lilienthal had been appointed to make further suggestions. It included only one scientist—J. Robert Oppenheimer, who had headed up the A-bomb development program at Los Alamos, a man whom Groves did not admire.

It was Oppenheimer who made the observation soon after Hiroshima that "the atom bomb is something against which *no* defense is possible, the 'secret' of which is only a matter of time—not more than a few years for some of them." The accuracy of his forecast was to be borne out in a very few years.

The ultimate jurisdiction over postwar control of atomic energy in America lay with Congress—not with the White House, the State Department, or the Pentagon. During the years following Hiroshima, many scientists were asked to appear before various Congressional committees. For the first time in our history, scores of scientists trekked up to Capitol Hill, where only a few distinguished individual scientific leaders like Bush and Conant had gone before.

These professional nuclear experts had had no previous contacts with Congressmen, so many had to make difficult adjustments. Most of the Congressmen, likewise, felt uncomfortable in the Committee hearing rooms with the scientists. The legislators were far happier with engineers, who they felt were more like "hardheaded businessmen."

Many conservative Congressmen, finding themselves for the first time involved with nuclear scientists, felt that these men from the laboratories were actually in touch with a supernatural world of awesome forces, a world which they alone could control. The nuclear scientists' understanding of the atom and its forces, a knowledge restricted to their own small coterie, marked the scientists as men set apart.

Senator Millard Tydings of Maryland admitted to Leo Szilard in late 1945 that if the same hearings had been held in 1939 he imagined "the scientists would have been called a lot of crackpots . . . and visionaries playing with theories." But after the vivid application of atomic theories in the incineration of two Japanese cities this feeling was no longer evident in Congress. Other Senators, like Richard Russell of Georgia, looked upon the scientists like "a country boy going to the M.D. He thinks the doc can do anything."

Some Senators, like Bourke Hickenlooper of Iowa wished that the problem had never arisen and that it would go away. His comment to Bush on the release of atomic energy was cryptic: "We have got to the point when we have rubbed the lamp and the genie has come out and we cannot get him to go back into the lamp." Even the astute young Senator J. William Fulbright, later to become the distinguished chairman of the Foreign Relations Committee, tacitly agreed with Dr. Isador I. Rabi, the Nobel laureate, who complained that Congress made the scientists feel like a "special" class of citizen. Fulbright explained: "The reason is that you scientists scared us all to death with your atomic bomb and we are still very frightened about it."

Dr. Harry S. Hall, who made a study of the relationship between the scientists and our conservative national legislators during the 1945–48 period, observed that many of the Congressmen looked upon the scientists as long-bearded foreigners with garlic on their breaths. It was true that most of the top nuclear scientists like Teller, Fermi, Szilard, Wigner, Bethe, and others were recent emigrés. Communication between them and the Congressmen thus was frequently difficult and awkward, and contributed to the lawmakers' false stereotyping of the men. Because *no one* in either of the two houses was a scientist, it was impossible for members of Congress to be objective in their relationship with and evaluation of these wizards of the atom.

One Senator termed the nuclear scientists "new, queer, bipeds from abroad" and another looked upon them as "men from another world colliding with a new area of politics." The fact that all of the basic findings concerning the atom came from scientists from foreign countries only served to heighten the distrust and suspicion of many Congressmen. Few could understand Wigner's thick accent and Szilard was called "way up there" by another legislator who couldn't even pronounce his name correctly.

Because almost all of these scientists were foreign-born, they were, *ipso facto,* un-American to many Congressmen. As Representative John Rankin of Mississippi put it after listening to five scientists testify in a row: "Not one is a REAL American!" Another of his colleagues chimed in with: "Aren't there any good old-fashioned American names here?" There was dead silence in the stuffy committee room. No one answered.

The nationalistic feeling built up during four years of war was still at a high pitch in Washington and explained some of the superpatriotic remarks made by these Congressmen. They were only revealing the insecurity which stemmed from their own scientific ignorance and their jealousy over the fact that the scientists possessed knowledge about the atom that even they—with all their security clearances—did not.

Some Congressmen looked upon these scientists as a secret society of "priests" who lived apart from the rest of society. As "mystics" and keepers of scientific "mysteries," it was even thought they could bar others from their cult. This caused several Congressmen to express fears that the scientists might betray us if crossed. This fear, compounded with the fear of possible subversion, produced an uneasiness in Congress about leaving the scientists alone without "adequate supervision." As one suspicious member of the Special Senate Committee argued, "One reason for the difficulty is the very psychology of the scientists themselves. . . . It is second nature for them to talk and divulge everything they know. . . . There is an instantaneous communication between scientists with all barriers down."

A final, subtle factor operating to distort the true picture of atomic science in the postwar period was the prejudice shown by many members of the Congress against the great number of refugee Jewish atomic scientists. Although no legislator went on record publicly on this point, many were particularly disturbed when the Jewish scientists took the lead in the battle for civilian control of atomic energy later embodied in the McMahon Bill. Congressmen from the formerly isolationist sections of the Midwest, Southwest, and West, who were supporting the May-Johnson military atomic-control bill were outraged by the support of the Jewish scientists for the appointment of David Lilienthal, an American Jew, as the first head of the yet unborn Atomic Energy Commission. This anti-Semitic feeling, held by only a minority of Congressmen, often caused the prejudiced men to view all scientists as an alien constellation. Despite these misunderstandings, one of the amazing things about this period was that the scientists were consulted by Congress at all.

Because most of the nuclear scientists first saw the problem of the international control of atomic energy as primarily a *technical* one, in their appearances before various Congressional committees they vociferously denied that they were advocates of a *political* position. During the height of the struggle to convert the U.S. Senate to the principle of international control of the atom, the president of the Federation of Atomic Scientists stated: "The Federation makes a point of being nonpolitical . . . To hell with politics. The question is: Are you pro- or anti-suicide?"

The scientists had found an ally in Democratic Senator Brien McMahon of Connecticut, who had become convinced of the necessity of civilian control of postwar atomic energy. He persisted until a majority of his colleagues were convinced that his proposed legislation was more in the nation's interest than the May-Johnson Bill. With the scientists' support, the McMahon Act was passed in July, 1946, and a civilian-controlled Atomic Energy Commission was born. The passage of this remarkable piece of legislation was accomplished in less than one-third of the time normally needed to get similar laws enacted. This act was a dual tribute to the scientists' prodding and the vision of Congress.

So the scientists won their battle for civilian control over national atomic energy output. In the international arena, however, they failed. They still retained faint hopes of transferring the national monopoly to an international control agency sometime in the future. The scientists' conviction of the rightness of their cause, together with their newfound prestige, impressed Washington greatly and helped to educate the nation and the world in the worthiness of their ultimate goal.

In 1947, President Truman recognized the need for a full examination of the nation's scientific research effort and established the President's Science Research Board, under the chairmanship of his business adviser, John R. Steelman. In that year, many significant changes took place in the organization of the Federal government for science. Old agencies were reorganized, new ones appeared, and programs expanded rapidly.

The infant AEC grew fast and was soon to become second only to the Defense Department in the magnitude of its basic and applied scientific research activities. The transfer of the Manhattan District from military to civilian control did not occur until 1947, with the last of the contracts being shifted over to the AEC by 1948. Although the majority of its research would continue to be conducted in Government-owned facilities for the next decade, it had already established a mode of operation through research and development contracts with industry and universities.

When the Department of Defense was established in 1947, with the addition of the new independent Department of the Air Force, Congress gave the first Secretary of Defense, James Forrestal, the broad responsibility of unifying the three service departments and eliminating unnecessary duplication, particularly in R&D. A new R&D Board was therefore set up to report to the Secretary of Defense. It had two representatives from each department and a civilian chairman, appointed by the Secretary. Its mission was to prepare an integrated military R&D program and to give advice on trends in scientific research.

This R&D Board was assisted by a staff of several hundred military and civilian personnel, supplemented by the efforts of over 2,000 consultants. A network of committees and panels was created, consisting mainly of scientists outside the Government, to review the scientific programs and to recommend an appropriate R&D budget to the Secretary of Defense. They also developed a system of classifying the military R&D effort into categories and programs and relating these to the operational needs of the military services.

This R&D Board had control over our nation's *major* science efforts in the postwar years, and it performed a useful function by providing a forum where the many diverse viewpoints of the three services could be heard and acceptable compromises reached.

But the scientists were still greatly concerned with the *non-military* aspects of the Government's interest in science. After five years of persistent lobbying by scientific interest groups, Congress established the National Science Foundation in 1950. NSF was set up only after extensive legislative hearings had been held and Capitol Hill was convinced that the overwhelming majority of the nation's scientists, industrialists, and educators favored such an agency. Congress was in no rush to approve the NSF, as it had been with the establishment of the AEC four years earlier.

Dr. Alan Waterman was named director of this new small organization whose specific mission was "to develop a national science policy for the promotion of basic research and for education in the sciences." One of the duties of this new scientific foundation was to provide grants to universities for the investigation and improvement of science teaching. In the beginning, the hesitancy of the NSF to assume the authority given to it stemmed from a shortage of funds and Waterman's reluctance to move ahead with vigor.

A typical comparison of the Congressional scientific allocations can be seen in the grants for the year 1953. A mere $3½ million was granted to the NSF for R&D work, while the Department of Defense received $1.5 billion for the same purpose. Waterman, in a 1953 speech, pointed out the future implications of this disparity. He noted that the U.S. was spending $350 million on scientific contract projects at universities and laboratories, of which the NSF's contribution was only $1,700,-000. With most of the Pentagon's contracts going for *applied* research, offset only by the modest *basic* research funds allotted by the small NSF, the potential menace to the freedom of our universities under this kind of military financial control was readily apparent to many alarmed onlookers.

In the five years following the end of World War II, America had established three new and significant governmental science agencies: The AEC, the NSF, and the reorganized military R&D efforts of the Pentagon. Never before had we accomplished so many major scientific organizational advances in such a short period. The relationship between science and Government appeared harmonious, but behind the scenes the two giants were sowing seeds of mutual distrust.

As long as our atomic monopoly remained unchallenged, serenity held sway in Washington. We were the undisputed No. 1 world power, and we hoped to maintain that perch for some time to come. How long would it last? Some experts predicted that it would be 10 to 20 years before any other nation could achieve an atomic bomb. Were these soothsayers correct in their judgment? We did not have to wait long to find out.

# Chapter 3

# Disillusionment with the Super
# 1946-1956

For the scientists who hoped to see their atomic brainchild used only in peaceful pursuits, the decade following World War II was a bitter period. Upon the explosion of the first Russian A-bomb in September of 1949, America's supposed atomic monopoly disappeared with the Soviet mushroom cloud. American complacency was shattered; and the Russian achievement spurred debate as to whether American scientists should speed up attempts to create a "superbomb" to regain our atomic monopoly. As it became apparent that, with an atomic-fission bomb to trigger the fusion, a thermonuclear bomb was possible, a struggle arose within the scientific fraternity over whether to recommend a go-ahead.

Two schools of thought developed out of the struggle. One group wanted bigger bombs—symbolized by the H-bomb—with the idea of "massive retaliation" as our main deterrent to war. This school was led by two brilliant and difficult men—Dr. Edward Teller and Dr. Ernest O. Lawrence.

The other school, led by Oppenheimer, Bush, and Rabi, felt that this was a totally inadequate answer to our dilemma, since a decision to build the H-bomb would lead America into believing that this was all that was necessary to counter the Russian threat. They also felt that the H-bomb, if developed, would be more valuable to the Russians than to us, for the U.S. offered better targets. Our effort would obviously impel the Russians to follow suit, ending the possibility of any future American-Soviet agreement on atomic control and disarmament, this school thought.

29

As chairman of the AEC's powerful General Advisory Committee from October, 1949, to January, 1950, Oppenheimer felt that it would be wiser from a military viewpoint to build more A-bombs with the available facilities. It was pointed out that even if the H-bomb could be made, it would produce a lesser "bang for a buck" than an equivalent number of A-bombs. The General Advisory Committee went along with Oppenheimer almost unanimously, as did three of the five members of the AEC, with Gordon Dean and Chairman Lewis L. Strauss dissenting.

Teller, however, still held out for the immediate institution of a "crash" program. He had been removed from his work at Los Alamos and was mortally offended because his offspring, the thermonuclear weapon, had not been blessed by Oppenheimer. Lawrence and Dr. Luis Alvarez of the Berkeley science group were in sympathy with Teller. They had previously been disappointed when their plans for the construction of the H-bomb were turned down in Washington in September, 1949, after the announcement of the successful blast of the Russian "Joe I" A-bomb. They naïvely believed that the development of the H-bomb would proceed "automatically" after this disclosure. The scientists were also miffed at their former university colleague, who they felt had grown too egotistical after he left them for Los Alamos in 1943.

President Truman finally accepted the minority views of Teller and Strauss, the new chairman of the Atomic Energy Commission, and rejected the majority views of the General Advisory Committee of scientists who had accepted their social responsibility and given their policy advice in a forthright manner. They had based their advice on "social theory" and not on technical facts. When the Truman Administration rejected the suggestions made by these scientists in 1952 regarding their opposition to the proposed development of the hydrogen bomb, it signified the failure of the political leadership in Washington to develop a responsible and realistic foreign and social policy regarding nuclear weapons.

But proponents of the H-bomb concept Lawrence and Teller, whom Oppenheimer called "two experienced promoters," also had a theory of their own concerning the aggressive nature of Soviet intentions and the outcome of the nuclear arms race. Although they won the first round, this group of scientists failed to realize the long-range political implications of their efforts.

A few leading voices continued to oppose the testing of the first hydrogen bomb, while its development was officially under way. Vannevar Bush tried to persuade Government officials to seek an H-bomb test ban with the Soviet Union in 1952, before any tests had taken place. But he was overruled; and work continued on the development of what came to be called "The Super."

For 18 months after the White House decision, it looked as if Oppenheimer's views were even better founded than he knew. Achievement of an H-bomb appeared increasingly more dubious, and it became virtually certain that what had been contemplated could never be made to work. But in June, 1951, Teller came up with a brilliant discovery that made a technical breakthrough possible. Oppenheimer waxed enthusiastic over Teller's invention and helped the project along. Teller admitted that Oppenheimer had contributed an idea at this time "not very ingenious but . . . very useful" that is embodied in today's H-weapons.

Even so, Oppenheimer continued to insist that the H-bomb was not the whole answer and he continued to push in a fiercely energetic manner for projects concerned with continental defense, radar warnings, and the tactical and strategic use of A-bombs. He soon aroused the wrath of the Air Force by saying that thermonuclear massive retaliation against Russian cities should not be the end-all of our policy. His plea for a more versatile, flexible atomic arsenal with tactical application served only to increase the enmity toward him within the Strategic Air Command, which was flying high in the Pentagon at the time. (Oppenheimer's views were finally adopted as new national defense policy a decade later by Secretary of Defense

Robert McNamara, and General Maxwell D. Taylor, chairman of the Joint Chiefs of Staff, in the Kennedy Administration.)

General Roscoe Wilson, former commandant of the Air War College, expressed worry over Oppenheimer's "pattern of action." This pattern led Wilson to go to the Director of Military Intelligence to express "concern" that Dr. Oppenheimer was interested in the internationalization of atomic energy at a time when the United States had a monopoly.

Most active of all Oppenheimer's Air Force opponents, however, was their chief scientist, David T. Griggs. He once admitted to Oppenheimer that he had impugned the older man's loyalty, whereupon the atom-bomb scientist called him a "paranoid"—which doubtless did little to win Griggs's favor. Griggs later testified that he saw a 1952 summer scientific study project at Cambridge, Massachusetts, as a plot engineered by a "secret junta," to undercut SAC and deny it the fat slice of the defense budget it might otherwise obtain. He testified that an M.I.T. scientist, Dr. Jerrold R. Zacharias, had written the mystic letters ZORC on the blackboard at a scientific meeting, and explained that they stood for Zacharias, Oppenheimer, Rabi, and Charles Lauritsen, another famous scientist. The implication was that this cabal of intriguers had plotted to damage SAC.

Zacharias and the others denied Griggs's accusation and no verification ever appeared in the record. The sinister ZORC story, the first public attack on Oppenheimer, appeared in the May, 1952, issue of *Fortune* magazine. The research material came directly from the Air Force Chief of Staff, General Hoyt Vandenberg. By that time, Teller's invention had put the H-bomb's possibilities in a new light, and Oppenheimer was vulnerable for his 1949 anti-H-bomb recommendation. The heat was on.

Events moved to a grand climax. At dawn on November 1, 1952, "Mike," our first H-bomb, was detonated on the Pacific island of Elugelab. After the flaming fireball of the first *Super*—rated at three megatons—had disappeared, the observers were shocked to discover that a crater one mile long and 175 feet deep had been dug into the Pacific where the island used to be. The H-bomb was a stark success.

The respected Vannevar Bush felt that we had just lost our second chance at negotiating with Russia. "The test marked our entry into a very disagreeable type of world," he said. ". . . I still think that we made a grave error in conducting that test at that time, and not attempting to make a simple agreement with Russia. I think history will show that was a turning point; that when we entered into the grim world we are entering right now, that those who pushed that thing through to a conclusion without making that attempt have a great deal to answer for."

Although our first H-bomb detonation was not made public for more than a year, its secret could not be kept forever. After our next "Bravo" series H-bomb test explosions were triggered in the mid-Pacific in 1954, the findings from the chemical and physical analysis of fish caught in the detonation area convinced many scientists that AEC Chairman Strauss was trying to hide the dangerous nature of the atomic arms race from the American people. Very few scientists publicly supported the Government policy of denial and deceit. They had their revenge against Strauss when they successfully supported Senator Clinton Anderson of New Mexico in his opposition to Strauss's appointment as Secretary of Commerce in the Eisenhower Administration.

The year 1954 also witnessed a behind-the-scenes struggle, finally bursting into the open with the sensational public disclosures in the Oppenheimer case, on the development of the H-bomb.

The 993-page volume, *In the Matter of J. Robert Oppenheimer,* which was published by the Government in July, 1954, unfolded a tragic Shakespearean plot illustrating the frustrations and problems of the spectators as well as of the central figures in the drama of the atom. In this historic and controversial 750,000-word document, America saw for the first time scientist pitted against scientist. The core of the case against Oppenheimer involved two matters, and they occupied almost equal portions of the official Government transcript. One was the Haakon Chevalier episode. The other concerned the defendant's views on the hydrogen "superbomb."

The official charge against Oppenheimer was contained in a letter sent to him in early 1954 by AEC Manager Kenneth D. Nichols. Nichols stated that from 1945 to 1949 the scientific chief of our A-bomb project had considered construction of the hydrogen bomb feasible, but that, following the explosion of the first Russian atomic bomb, he opposed the development of the hydrogen bomb because it was not feasible, because it was politically undesirable, because it was immoral, and because there were not enough skilled scientists and facilities for its development. He was also charged with continued opposition and lack of cooperation even after President Truman had decided to push the project.

A special Personnel Security Board, consisting of Gordon Gray, former Secretary of the Army (Chairman); Thomas A. Morgan, President of the Sperry Corporation; and R. Ward Evans, professor of chemistry at Loyola University, was appointed to hear evidence on the charges leveled against Oppenheimer. The Board, which was popularly known as the Gray Board, met in Chicago from April 12 to May 6, 1954. In their report to the AEC, the investigators gave no credence to William Borden's letter, which had triggered the entire investigation.

On November 7, 1953, Borden, former executive director of the Joint Congressional Committee on Atomic Energy, wrote a letter based solely on derogatory information contained in the FBI files on Oppenheimer. Borden sent the letter, in which he implied that the scientist had opposed the H-bomb effort in 1949 because he was a "Soviet agent," to FBI Director J. Edgar Hoover, who distributed the letter to top Government officials. The conclusions reached by Borden were so baseless and false that they received no mention in the final report of the Personnel Security Board.

In defense of Oppenheimer, the grand old man of American science, Dr. Vannevar Bush, roared to the Gray Board that it should have refused to entertain such a charge and should have sent Kenneth Nichols' letter back to the AEC manager for redrafting. "The letter," he said, "is quite capable of being interpreted as placing a man on trial, because he held opinions and had the temerity to express them. If this country ever gets to the point where we come that near to the Russian system, we are certainly not in any condition to attempt to lead the free world towards the benefits of democracy!"

The M.I.T. chairman concluded his testimony with these stirring remarks: "I think this board or no board should ever sit on a question in this country of whether a man should serve his country or not because he expressed strong opinions. If you want to try that case, you can try me. I have expressed strong opinions many times, and I intend to do so. They have been unpopular opinions at times. When a man is pilloried for doing that, this country is in a severe state."

The Board did not concur with Bush. Thirty-nine more witnesses were called before the hearings were concluded. Such eminent men as Dr. James B. Conant of Harvard, Ambassador George Kennan, Dr. Hans Bethe, head of the Theoretical Division at Los Alamos, Gordon Dean, David Lilienthal, Norris Bradbury, Oppenheimer's successor at Los Alamos; ten former and present members of the General Advisory Committee, including Dr. Rabi, its chairman; and John J. McCloy, Assistant Secretary of War and civilian head of the Manhattan Project—all spoke strongly in Oppenheimer's defense.

During the three and a half weeks of testimony, the Board discovered no treasonable motive on Oppenheimer's part and no positive acts to delay the H-bomb project after the White House gave the green light in January, 1950. Yet, some members of the Board retained misgivings about Oppenheimer, the man. These doubts spilled over in their final report.

By a vote of 2 to 1 (with Evans, the lone scientist on the board, dissenting), the Gray Board concluded Oppenheimer's security clearance should be revoked because he had delayed the development of the H-bomb by not trying energetically to encourage scientists to join the project at Los Alamos and had failed to be enthusiastic about it. Gray and Morgan felt that Oppenheimer's activities had sinister and disloyal motivations, and that as a Government servant and consultant he had betrayed a trust by deliberately opposing national policy.

Evans, the dissenter, who favored restoring Oppenheimer's clearance, put the matter in a nutshell: "He did not hinder the development of the H-bomb and there is absolutely NOTHING in the testimony to show that he did!"

The majority of the Gray Board convicted Oppenheimer primarily on the grounds of his association with Haakon Chevalier, a professor of French at the University of California at Berkeley. Because he was one of Oppenheimer's Communist-tinged, "parlor-pink" friends, the Board utilized the McCarthy tactic of deciding guilt by association. Oppenheimer admitted that he had been an "idiot" when he told one lie to a security officer in 1943 to protect Chevalier. He said he had concocted a "cock and bull" story to cover up the single contact made by George Eltenton, a British scientist, who had once spoken to him (Oppenheimer) about the possibility of transmitting technical information to Soviet scientists.

Colonel Boris Pash, the security officer at Los Alamos, who never had any dealings with Oppenheimer beyond one interview on the Chevalier affair, told the board that he still "questioned" Oppenheimer's "loyalty." This doubt was expressed in spite of the fact that the Soviets were then our allies and that Oppenheimer had related the true story to General Groves in December, 1943.

The release of the Gray report provoked an immediate storm of criticism and contempt for the Board's findings among an influential segment of the press and other leading voices of opinion. The AEC voted 4 to 1 to confirm the Gray Board's findings (with only Henry D. Smyth dissenting). The majority, including AEC Chairman Lewis Strauss, vehemently insisted that Oppenheimer's attitude toward the H-bomb issue had utterly no bearing on their findings (except for a question of Oppenheimer's candor in his testimony about it).

In his separate opinion condemning Oppenheimer, AEC member Thomas Murray rejected with devastating argument the Gray-Morgan majority viewpoint, stating that "in both political and technical respects he has been proved wrong; nothing further need be said." Actually, Oppenheimer's technical views were both right and wrong. In 1949, he was correct in his notion that the H-bomb could not be built, until Teller's breakthrough, when he was wrong. Oppenheimer's stand on the political issue is still subject to debate and will have to await the judgment of history. Many astute observers could not share Murray's dogmatic views on the matter.

The AEC majority denounced Oppenheimer for visiting Chevalier in Paris, since they felt that he risked being kidnaped by Russian agents while there. One AEC member even admitted that the case against Oppenheimer hinged on this point.

In his dissenting opinion, Henry Smyth remarked that, if one started with the assumption that Oppenheimer was "disloyal," then the incidents brought up in the hearings might arouse suspicion. But, if one made the opposite assumption, then the Chevalier affair was perfectly logical, for the incident showed the unwillingness of a man to snitch on his friend. Even General Groves admitted that he thought Oppenheimer was "acting in the typical American schoolboy attitude that there is something wicked about telling on a friend. I do know this: That he was doing what he thought was essential, WHICH WAS TO DISCLOSE TO ME THE DANGERS OF THIS PARTICULAR ATTEMPT (OF A POTENTIAL SPY) TO ENTER THE PROJECT." Groves even conceded that Oppenheimer was most valuable and "did a magnificent job as far as the war effort was concerned."

There had been other persons who were far more deeply involved in the Communist conspiracy, as agents, spies, and traitors, than Oppenheimer. By acts of contrition and confession, men like Louis Budenz and Whittaker Chambers had won back the favor of many Americans; and it was hoped that it would also be possible in this historic case. The Gray Board noted that the nation owed Oppenheimer "a great debt of gratitude for loyal and magnificent service and for his enormous contribution to his country."

The AEC majority, however, was not impressed. Oppenheimer retired to the less controversial cloisters of the Institute of Advanced Study at Princeton where he remains to this day —outside of Government service. Dr. Rabi perhaps said it most aptly: "We had an A-bomb and a whole series of them . . . and what more do you want, mermaids? This A-bomb is just a tremendous achievement. If the end of the road is this kind of hearing, which can't help but be humiliating, I thought it was a pretty bad show. I still think so."

The Oppenheimer affair raised many questions about the relationship of Government and science which are yet unanswered. Why, for instance, were the four AEC members so savage in their denunciation of Oppenheimer? Why was the hearing conducted as a trial—which the rules of the AEC forbid—instead of an administrative inquiry following proper rules? Why was Chief Counsel Roger Robb so intent on degrading Oppenheimer? Why was the huge transcript released at all, and then so suddenly, after such a long silence on the matter? What was the real nature and purpose of our security program? Was it meant to be preventive or punitive?

In the light of Oppenheimer's record of loyalty and discretion since 1943, was the basis of the removal of his security clearance really the fear that he would disclose secrets in the future, either by design or by accident? Was this move realistic? Oppenheimer had as much security information in his head in 1954 as any man alive. The Government never answered the perplexing question as to how it was going to take away the "classified" secrets that had been stored in Oppenheimer's mind.

On the same day the United States government issued its transcripts on the Oppenheimer case, a small book called *Sci-*

*ence and the Common Understanding* appeared for sale. Its author was none other than J. Robert Oppenheimer, and the slim volume contained his six Reith Lectures delivered in 1953 over the British Broadcasting System. In one of them is an apt quotation written by a great man to a young friend: "Science can never be retrograde; what is once acquired of real knowledge can never be lost. To preserve the freedom of the human mind then and freedom of the press, every spirit should be ready to devote himself to martyrdom; for as long as we may think as we will, and speak as we think, the condition of man will proceed in improvement." Oppenheimer was quoting from a letter by Thomas Jefferson.

The Oppenheimer security trial bitterly accentuated the political breach within the scientific community and marked the end of the period of political innocence for the scientists. The Government had estranged many scientists. The implication that Oppenheimer couldn't be trusted, simply because he opposed our development of the hydrogen bomb, weakened the faith of our scientists in the competency and integrity of American political leadership.

For the first time in ten years of political activities, the restraining code of professional ethics which had governed scientists' earlier political actions was almost completely submerged as they let their passions of resentment and hostility come to the fore. Some physical scientists had committed the unpardonable sin of questioning a fellow scientist's personal integrity. While Oppenheimer took the brunt of these attacks, other scientists were not left untouched.

More than a decade after the birth of the atomic age, Dr. Eugene Rabinowitch observed, "Despite a certain relaxation of tensions which arose in the heyday of McCarthy . . . and the campaign that led to the effective elimination from public life of J. Robert Oppenheimer . . . American scientists remain, in 1956, a harassed profession, occupying a defensive position in the political arena. Their early hopes of playing an important role insuring world peace and prosperity are still in abeyance."

In September, 1956, the editor of the *Bulletin of Atomic Scientists* wrote in retrospect that scientists had proved themselves almost powerless in reforming the political world. Yet he optimistically believed that the antiscientific trend in the United States was bound to reverse itself. One year later, his wish came true, not as a *direct* result of any change of attitude within America itself, but, rather, *indirectly* from the impact of the beeps from a small Soviet sphere orbiting the earth.

# Chapter 4

# The Lull Before the Second Storm
# 1954-1957

In the wake of World War II, the consensus of the American people and the Government in Washington was for a return to prewar normalcy. Consumer demands, subordinated to the war effort, would now be met. In the era of public and political complacency following V-J Day, most of the nation's technological facilities were devoted to the production of washing machines, automobiles, and the new electronic marvel—television.

We felt fairly secure behind our growing stockpile of atomic bombs hidden in secret chambers around the nation. Even though we no longer had an atomic monopoly, we still had *more* and *bigger* bombs than our adversary. During the decade that followed the close of the most devastating war in our history we were not greatly concerned with any new military applications of science.

The Korean "police action" came and went without any rumbling on the scientific frontier. After all, didn't we fight the Communists to a standoff, using predominantly obsolete World War II weapons and without resorting to the use of the A-bomb? Except for the introduction of the subsonic jet fighter planes to duel with the Soviet MIGs, there were no significant scientific breakthroughs.

A few scientific prophets in the Pentagon and outside the Government foresaw a new technological problem on the horizon. Yet no one spoke out to challenge the supremacy of the atom. We were now living in the Atomic Age, and no scientist or nonscientist cried out in the wilderness to warn America about the implications of breakthroughs in rocketry.

The one man who might have sounded the warning was Dr. Goddard, but he had died a disillusioned man in 1945, before his dreams of going to the moon could be fulfilled. Dying of throat cancer, he had spent his last days during the war working for the Navy at Annapolis on small, one-man bazooka rocket weapons—a far cry from the big rockets he had built and flown a decade earlier at White Sands, New Mexico. Not adept at salesmanship, he had been unable to convince the military or anyone else in Washington of the necessity of working on the larger rockets that were soon to revolutionize both the science of weaponry and the power relationships of the world.

During the decade of national complacency that followed World War II, the public still looked upon rockets primarily as peaceful implements to lift fireworks into the sky on the Fourth of July. Meanwhile, behind closed doors in the Pentagon and unknown to most of America, a few Government agencies quietly began exploring the possibilities of using rockets for other purposes.

Back in 1944, at the request of General Henry H. Arnold, Chief of Staff of the Army Air Force, Dr. Theodore von Kármán of the Jet Propulsion Laboratory of the California Institute of Technology was asked to advise the U.S. Air Force on the role of new technical developments in jet propulsion, supersonic aerodynamics, electronics, and other military fields. On December 15, 1945, his committee issued a report called "Toward New Horizons" in which it prophesied events that it thought would come to pass a decade later.

The Hungarian scientific genius Von Kármán suggested that the Air Force set up the following 10-year goals: supersonic flight; pilotless aircraft (the pre-space age term for "guided missiles"); all-weather flying; perfected navigation and communication; remote-controlled fighter and bomber forces; and aerial transportation of entire armies. His committee's recommendations, made two years before the first supersonic flight took place, led to the establishment of the Arnold Engineering Development Center at Tullahoma, Tennessee, Eglin Field in Florida, and Edwards Air Force Base in California.

The Hungarian scientist's 1945 conceptions of our future intercontinental missiles unfortunately missed the mark. He perceived them as either a high-altitude, jet-propelled, Mach 2 (1,400 mph) bomber under automatic control (similar to the later ill-fated *Navaho*) or as an ultra-stratospheric rocket with wings for extending its range by gliding (a concept borrowed from the German concept of a winged V-2 rocket). The development of intercontinental ballistic missiles was not foreseen at all by the Von Kármán group of scientists, a group that in 1945 included Dr. Hugh Dryden, head of the Government's National Advisory Committee on Aeronautics.

Between its establishment in 1915 and the postwar period, the National Advisory Committee on Aeronautics had built three large wind tunnels for testing aircraft models. While Dr. Dryden was attending to the administrative chores, his top assistant, Dr. John Victory, NACA's first employee, usually took care of obtaining the needed annual funds from Congress. As appropriations time drew near each year, Victory, a shrewd scientist-turned-lobbyist, would round up key Congressmen and lure them on an "inspection trip" to the Ames Laboratory in California, to the Lewis Labs at Cleveland, or to Langley Field in Virginia. These were the three main NACA laboratories. These trips were necessary to educate the Congressmen about the Government's aviation research projects and to justify the expenditure of an annual budget which by 1958 had reached $100,000,000.

NACA had been delegated the responsibility to "supervise and direct the scientific study of the problems of flight, with a view to their practical solution. . . ." NACA research was designed to be useful to both the nonmilitary and the military segments of aeronautics. The entire operation was based on the premise that teamwork provided the surest guarantee of progress in aeronautics. Some 500 scientific experts served without compensation on the 28 different technical committees through which NACA coordinated the great complex of American aviation and rocket research.

The 1949 Von Kármán report had conservatively estimated that chemical rockets "might" be made with ranges up to 30 times that of the German V-2 rocket. Strangely enough, only *one* sentence in the whole report was devoted to a "satellite being a definite possibility." Seventeen years later, Dryden, now the Deputy Director of NASA, apologetically admitted that "neither Von Kármán nor I had a very enviable record about foreseeing the present development of astronautics. We were rather conservative engineers. On the 50th anniversary of flight in 1953, I proposed that taking into consideration the speed at which guided missiles travel, that at which models have been propelled, the experimental data available from hypersonic experiments in wind tunnels and ranges, and the theoretical calculations which have been made, *we may reasonably suppose that a satellite vehicle is entirely practicable now and that travel to the moon is attainable in the next 50 years.*" (Author's italics.) Fifteen years would have been a more accurate estimate in light of present progress.

A year later, in 1954, Von Kármán made an equally unenviable prediction. Alluding to manned space travel in his book *Aerodynamics,* he wrote: "I do not want to be either too skeptical or too enthusiastic. . . . It is improbable that a return [to earth] can be achieved without using rocket power as a brake. This of course means an enormous amount of fuel reserve. It appears to me that the use of nuclear energy will make the rocket so much more efficient that *serious* attempts to build a spaceship should await the advent of the nuclear rocket. . . . Perhaps the effort necessary to proceed from the present-day long-range, high-altitude rocket to a manned space rocket is no more than the effort which led from the Wright brothers' airplane of 1903 to today's supersonic aircraft."

These conservative estimates and mistaken notions about the future of spaceflight actually impeded scientific progress in this area at the higher echelons in the Pentagon. Yet Von Kármán did make a positive contribution—probably his greatest—by bridging the gap between technology and the military, thereby creating the present defense system that has enabled the free world to survive and prosper. He and General Arnold not only used technology to create superior airpower as exemplified in SAC during the 1950's, but they also took the lead in educating the military into a technical literacy that enabled them to work more effectively with the technical community.

In the summer of 1953, two 39-year-old physicists, Dr. Simon Ramo and Dr. Dean Wooldridge, left their positions as vice-presidents of Hughes Aircraft in California because of dissatisfaction with the management. They each invested $6,700 of their own money and set up a one-room office in what is now a barber shop in suburban Los Angeles. These two Ph.D. scientists, who had met as graduate engineering students at the California Institute of Technology more than a decade earlier, started out with a card table, a chair, a telephone, a rented typewriter, and a secretary. Little did they realize that their budding enterprise also marked the birth of a new type of scientist-adviser for the U.S. government.

The origin of the Ramo-Wooldridge Corporation coincided with the rebirth of the Air Force's intercontinental ballistic missile (ICBM) program. The "thermonuclear breakthrough" whereby the large H-bomb warhead could be successfully miniaturized, achieved by the late Dr. John von Neumann in 1952–53, brought about an abrupt change of thinking on the potentialities of the long-range missile. With the possibilities of reduction in the size and weight of the warhead now on the immediate horizon, the long-delayed working compact of the nuclear scientist with the rocket engineer was about to be signed.

Under the prodding of fiery young Trevor Gardner, special assistant to the Secretary of the Air Force, the Strategic Missiles Evaluation Committee was formed in October, 1953, to undertake a sweeping reassessment of a low-geared ICBM program in light of the new atomic technology. This committee of scientists was, naturally, headed by the brilliant Dr. von Neumann. Two of the eleven prominent members named to help him were none other than Dr. Simon Ramo and Dr. Dean Wooldridge. At the suggestion of Trevor Gardner, the infant Ramo-Wooldridge Corporation was given a contract to serve as the technical staff of the committee.

When the committee made its report on February 10, 1954, the Air Force and the Pentagon got a rude awakening. The old concepts of weapons technology were discarded as the scientists recommended a sharp acceleration of the nation's ICBM program, beginning with the *Atlas, Titan,* and *Thor* missiles. They also urged a new type of development-management organization to oversee the whole program. The scientists implied that the conventional "prime major contractor–sub-minor contractor" industrial pattern which had worked so well during World War II for building weapons systems would not work for a complex project of this magnitude.

The committee shared the feeling that no single industrial company had sufficient across-the-board competence in the physical sciences and other disciplines to manage the effort. So the Air Force set up a special organization called the Western Development Command in Inglewood, California, under young, upcoming Brigadier General Bernard Schriever, to push the development of the new unmanned military missiles—ICBMs and intermediate range ballistic missiles (IRBM).

The Air Force also broke precedent when it granted the technical supervision of the program to an independent agency. Because Ramo-Wooldridge's small cadre of bright young scientists and engineers had carried the ball so well up to this point, they were given the task. In a sense, they became the advisory "eyes and ears" of General Schriever for the next six years. When Ramo and his fellow scientists asked Congress for money to build a forest of expensive test stands at Cape Canaveral, Florida, for the IRBM–ICBM program in the mid-1950's as a safety factor in case several missiles exploded on the pad, they got their wish. Their argument for more testing of the big rockets won out. This new role was a far cry from their original advisory role. The scientists had, in this instance, become policy makers.

In a short time Ramo-Wooldridge became so "intimate" with the Air Force that it progressed far beyond its original advisory capacity of "systems engineering" on the missiles. Its scientists and engineers were even allowed to pry into the secrets of the various aero-space industries working on the three IRBM and ICBMs. Although the R-W Corporation was not allowed to compete with these big industries for the actual hardware building contracts, the corporation nevertheless soon aroused the collective wrath of the companies involved in the projects.

R-W blithely continued with its supervisory work for the Government despite these brickbats, since at that time none of its detractors could come up with an effective alternative to get the job done. Here was another example of the strange union of science and politics, with neither partner understanding or fully trusting the other, yet each equally dependent on the other for survival.

The Air Force's ballistics missile program, like the atom and hydrogen bomb projects before it, had welded a solid alliance between the Government and many of the nation's scientist-engineers, of which the R-W team happened to be only one glamorous example. As Dr. Harrison Brown, the prominent geochemist, bluntly put it: "Tens of thousands of scientists and technicians have devoted all of their professional lives to the invention and construction of weapons. A majority of those who went to work after World War II are convinced that weaponry is a way of life for themselves and expect the United States-Soviet contest to continue forever."

Meanwhile, in early 1957, President Eisenhower appointed a panel of sixty leading scientists and nonscientists, under the chairmanship of the late H. Rowan Gaither, Jr., chairman of the board of the Ford Foundation, to study the relative effectiveness of passive and active air defense. Dr. Jerome Wiesner, an electrical engineering professor at the Massachusetts Institute of Technology, was appointed technical director of the secret Gaither panel, which put in six months of intensive research.

Although the findings of the panel have remained secret to this day, its general recommendations have "leaked" out for public discussion. The group had made an exhaustive investigation of what the impact of a nuclear war on the United States would be. This project gave Wiesner and the panel members their first close look at the entire military posture of the country. The panel surveyed the possibilities of a nation-wide shelter program; the biological effects of radiation; the food, fuel and medical needs of the nation in the event of such a nuclear catastrophe; as well as ways to prevent looting in case of attack.

It foresaw the dangers of a military state, which would result in complete Government control of industry and labor, and the astronomical costs of an effective air and civil defense system. When President Eisenhower heard the stark findings of the Gaither panel, he told its members: "Gentlemen, you have left out only one thing. Where are the bulldozers we'll need for scraping the bodies off the streets?" Wiesner realized that we were in an arms race not only with the Russians but with ourselves as well. "The Russians were caught in the same trap," he said. "The more either side tried to buy security, the tighter the trap became."

On a cool October night a few months later the trap was sprung—and strangely enough, this time the atom had nothing to do with triggering the lever.

# Chapter 5

# Sputnik Spurs the Space Scientists
# 1957-1958

The atomic bomb pulled scientists to the fringes of the political arena, but *Sputnik* pushed science squarely into the field of politics. On October 4, 1957, the Soviet embassy in Washington held a reception in honor of the members of the International Rocket and Satellite Conference of the International Geophysical Year. At 5:58 P.M., Walter Sullivan, science editor of the New York *Times,* told Dr. Lloyd Berkner, chairman of the International Council of Scientific Unions, that a radio station on Long Island had detected the "beeps" of *Sputnik* I. Dr. Berkner interrupted the festivities to announce to his Russian colleagues the successful launching of a Soviet earth satellite. The international scientific setting of this dramatic announcement illuminated the purely scientific emphasis of America's early space efforts.

The immediate international scientific acclaim which greeted *Sputnik* was soon drowned in its political and military implications. First reactions ranged from the unfortunate description of the Soviet satellite as a "hunk of iron almost anybody could launch," by Admiral Arleigh Burke, chief of Naval Operations, to Presidential adviser Clarence Randall's "silly bauble" tag, to Dr. Edward Teller's warning of "Technological World War III." More sober observers, however, noted the political significance of the Soviet Union's technological advance. The new realm of space, whose problems had been confined within a small segment of the Government's military and scientific elite, had suddenly grown into a major national crisis involving the

Eisenhower Administration, the Congress, the scientific community, and the public at large in a political issue which was to permeate many facets of American life.

Faced with such a wide array of potent public pressures, the Administration formulated its response to *Sputnik.* In doing so, Eisenhower was forced to go to the scientific community for advice.

In the ten days after *Sputnik,* more scientists visited Eisenhower than in the previous ten months. This new access of scientists to the ranks of the high Government policy makers was the most obvious change in the Administration's style in the immediate post-*Sputnik* period. In October, Eisenhower decided to institutionalize this new relationship with the scientific community. On November 7, 1957, he announced the appointment of Dr. James R. Killian, president of M.I.T., as his special assistant for Science and Technology.

Killian was told that he was selected as the first presidential science adviser in our history because the President "wanted someone to help who wasn't involved in internal administration warfare. He wanted a consulting engineer, so to speak, with whom he could count on maintaining a confidential friendship."

The new adviser was also to serve as a responsible science reporter to the President, warning him of dangers and new advances. President Eisenhower had discovered, soon after *Sputnik,* that there was not *one* scientist in his administration to whom he could turn as a flabbergasted layman searching for an explanation of the real meaning of the dramatic cosmic event. From then on, science was no longer *persona non grata* at 1600 Pennsylvania Avenue.

Eisenhower had, by late November, moved the Science Advisory Committee from the Office of Defense Mobilization onto his White House Staff, thereby creating a multifaceted advisory structure for scientific and technological affairs. (The initial suggestion for the creation of PSAC came in the 1930's from the social scientists and not the physical scientists.)

The nation's immediate reaction to *Sputnik* provided these

two basic preconditions for more active scientific participation in future space policy making. Space had now become a major political issue. Certain politicians were anxious to include the scientists in the policy-making decisions which were to determine the size and organization of the country's future space effort. *Sputnik* had provoked the emergence of the scientists as important members of the national political system. Yet most of the scientists responded with uncertainty to the political challenges of space and remained essentially unsure of their space policy preferences throughout the subsequent months.

This indecision was rooted in most scientists' conflict of feelings toward space. Because of their participation in the International Geophysical Year and their sense of membership in an international professional community, most American scientists appreciated and admired the Russian space accomplishment. On the other hand, as Americans, they were concerned that their nation's scientific progress was rapidly being surpassed by that of the Soviet Union. Also, because they suspected that the Soviet Union had developed ICBMs, leading scientists such as Berkner viewed *Sputnik* as evidence of a USSR space threat to our national security. Torn between traditional respect for international scientific achievement and concern for America's welfare, top American scientists suddenly found themselves catapulted to positions of potential political influence.

The space scientists' political behavior throughout the post-*Sputnik* months was characterized by two important attributes. First, these scientific gladiators were entering the political arena with great prestige but an equally great lack of experience. Despite their new role, the scientists retained their profession's traditional reluctance to see science involved in politics. The authoritative journal *Science* set the tone when it editorialized in late November:

"Current emphasis on science in the thinking of . . . public leaders illustrates both a good trend and a bad habit. To have greater attention given to the welfare of science is good, but to have attitudes change so quickly and radically is a part of the inconsistent, on-and-off support that interferes seriously with steady scientific progress."

For the scientists, the political outburst following *Sputnik* I and II made any massive new effort in space, beyond that which they had earlier deemed professionally warranted, open to suspicion. The scientists also faced many unresolved questions which they considered more fundamental than the space problem. These questions related to the scientists' relations with the Federal government. In their public statements, they entered a general plea to American society to upgrade the status of science, and to this end they urged basic reforms along several fronts. Although there was no complete unanimity in their ranks, the majority called for Federal support of the educational system, increased Government support of the scientific input in weapons development, and better working conditions for scientists in federally supported projects of Government agencies. The Senate Preparedness Subcommittee, under Lyndon Johnson, also provided a public forum for the scientists.

Most leading scientific spokesmen virtually ignored the space issue as such. Indeed, their general comments upon the scientific challenge facing America contained only passing references to space. In testimony before the Senate Preparedness Subcommittee, Drs. Edward Teller and Vannevar Bush made only brief mention of space as a possible activity for expanded scientific effort. In discussing the potential organization of science in Government, Drs. Arthur Compton of Washington University and Lee DuBridge of the California Institute of Technology praised the Killian appointment but did not recommend assigning him any particular role in organizing the space program. Even the American Association for the Advancement of Science, the nation's major scientific organization, made *no* mention of a space program in the December 1957 report of its Parliament of Science. Yet most of the report was devoted to "science and public policy."

The high-ranking scientists—many of them working in close advisory capacities in Government—clearly ranked space exploration well below other scientific activities. Since most of them were physicists interested in basic scientific research or engineering college administrators concerned with fund raising, few were interested in space. Because of this professional bias and a desire to protect their concept of the Government's proper scientific mission, they attempted to dissuade other nonscientific political groups in Washington from precipitating a crash program in space. By early 1958, the President's new science advisers had shown that they would not be willing to jeopardize newfound general Federal support of *all* science by advocating a disproportionate expenditure on *space* science. So the issue was now joined. The discrepancy between the politicians' and scientists' evaluations of the importance of space was to affect the future role of the advisory scientists when NASA was established.

The magnitude and emphasis of any future space program and its organizational structure within the Government were the principal policy issues at stake. Our pre-*Sputnik* space program had been lodged almost entirely in the Department of Defense. The Office of Naval Research, under the policy guidance of the National Science Foundation and the National Academy of Sciences, had operational responsibility for the IGY *Vanguard* scientific earth satellite project. Since its inception, Project *Vanguard* had been a "purely" scientific venture and was denied top-priority status and regular fund allocations until late in 1957, when it was too late.

In the national furor that arose after *Sputnik,* these makeshift provisions appeared obviously inadequte to enable the United States to embark on any serious space race. As 1958 dawned, the administration, the powerful Senate Preparedness Subcommittee under Senator Johnson, the military services, and the scientific community, each independently concluded that some kind of permanent governmental organization for space was necessary. Their proposals differed, however, because of differing conceptions of the proper size and focus of the future space program.

The Office of the Secretary of Defense wished to retain our space efforts within the military services. Within this basic consensus, however, the civilian Defense officials and the Army favored a centralized Advanced Research Projects Agency (ARPA) for all research and development in advanced weaponry—including space. The Navy and Air Force, on the other hand, feared that such centralization would diminish their own roles and missions, and strongly argued in favor of leaving the space mission in each of the respective service R&D organizations. Even though Secretary of Defense Neil H. McElroy announced the forthcoming establishment of ARPA on November 15, competition for the military space mission continued within the Department of Defense.

Primarily as a result of the Preparedness Subcommittee's Missiles and Satellites Inquiry, Congress felt the Eisenhower Administration had seriously underestimated the significance of scientific research for military systems, and the political and prestige factors in a space program. In January, the committee's report suggested the establishment of an independent space agency, either within or outside the Department of Defense, to effectively pursue a national space program. Subsequently, Senator Lyndon Johnson, Democratic majority leader who spearheaded the Congressional space effort, came out in favor of an independent civilian agency.

The scientists reluctantly also came to support an independent space agency. While still retaining their initial ambivalence about space, the scientific community finally recognized that the Government was really embarking upon a comprehensive space program, and therefore they moved to represent their views both to the public and to Killian's office.

In the six months between the launching of *Sputnik* and the announcement of the administration's space agency bill, various scientific organizations offered unsolicited proposals ranging from an Astronautics R&D board proposed by the American Rocket Society, to a suggestion by the Federation of American Scientists that the organization and exploitation of outer space be under the AEC's jurisdiction. Although varied in scope and organizational detail, each of these basically similar proposals suggested an independent Federal space agency or commission *outside* the Department of Defense, using either the existing National Advisory Committee on Aeronautics (NACA) or the Atomic Energy Commission as models. Furthermore, each proposal emphasized that the *scientific* aspects of space exploitation were more important than either the military or political aims. Most groups wanted to restrict the activities of the proposed new agency to nonmilitary projects.

Dr. Hugh Dryden, director of NACA, warned his fellow scientists in January, 1958, that "the basic reason underlying these proposals for a new civilian agency is plain. The scientific community, understandably, is worried about the possibility that the extremely important nonmilitary aspects of space technology should be submerged or perhaps even lost if included as a mere adjunct to a military program."

Of all these proposals, the joint statement of the American Rocket Society and the Rocket and Satellite Research Panel of the National Academy of Science, made on January 4, 1958, was perhaps the most authoritative reflection of the scientific community's interest in space. The statement issued a call for a unified National Space Establishment to undertake scientific exploration of space, specifically excluding space weapon development and military operations, which would remain in the Pentagon. The authors of this proposal considered it "strongly desirable that the National Space Establishment be given statutory status as an independent agency in order that its work . . . be freely directed toward broad cultural, scientific, and commercial objectives . . . [which] transcend the short-term, though vitally important, military rocket missions of the DOD [Department of Defense].

Their proposal listed a timetable of space projects to be pursued in the subsequent decade and outlined the relative distinction between the missions of the civilian agency and the DOD in space. The only reference to future coordination between the Government agencies was that there should be "clear channels for mutual cooperation . . . in order to assure no jeopardy of short-term, vital military need on the one hand, and . . . maximum rate of advance of space research on the other."

The proposal depicted space as an "endless frontier," offering meteorological, agricultural, communicational, commercial, navigational, medical, and biological aids to man's life. Many would be of military value, but the sponsors argued that "their greater value would be to the civilian community at large," as the telephone had been.

This scientific organizational proposal assumed that the limits of military operations in space could be clearly demarcated from the civilian, thereby permitting streamlined, civil-military liaison. The scientists definitely envisaged the civilian agency as the single source of over-all planning and basic research in the national space effort. The military was to develop space vehicles only for specific military requirements which would be proved feasible by the prior research efforts of the civilian agency. By implication, a proper and correct division of military and civilian functions in space would be based upon agreement between military and civilian scientists as to what constituted military requirements.

The joint proposal's basic premise was that potential scientific achievement would be the basis for selection among all the possible space projects, beyond those few which had clear military relevance. Strangely enough, the authors considered *no* other criterion for initiating any specific space project. In other words, they were proposing a primarily research-oriented agency—at the expense of any political, economic, psychological, or military aspects of space missions.

The Eisenhower Administration, beleaguered by conflicting public demands for more action in space and, specifically, some sort of space agency, began searching for a solution that would simultaneously allay political competition for the control of space and satisfy its own strategic and budgetary requirements.

To find this solution, President Eisenhower turned to a small group of policy makers in the executive offices: Killian and his staff, the President's Science Advisory Committee (PSAC), and the Bureau of the Budget. The White House scientific advisers were in a unique position to best present the interests of their professional community.

The policy-making process which began just after the launching of *Sputnik II* on November 3, was a relatively secretive one. Initial discussion about various organizational alternatives took place in Dr. Killian's office and in the Space Sciences Panel of PSAC (pronounced PEE'-SAC). The outlines of an expanded and accelerated space program which emerged from the deliberations in December placed the civilian and scientific space missions within an enlarged NACA and left military space programs in the Department of Defense. By January, this was the position of the PSAC. On this basis, Killian asked the director of the Bureau of the Budget to launch organizational and administrative planning for the space program.

This solution clearly reflected the desire of the scientific community for a primarily civilian agency in which basic research and important peaceful space missions could be pursued free of military control. Besides providing such an agency structure, NACA had the nucleus of research facilities and staff, which could be expanded at a rate the scientific advisers considered consistent with the over-all scientific interests of the Government. This was a false solution, however, since there was no attempt to delineate the dividing line between the military and civilian areas of space.

PSAC's proposals stemmed from its conception of the goals of the space program. Not only did the committee emphasize scientific research in space; it specifically downgraded the potential military usefulness of outer space. As PSAC's 1958 report, *An Introduction to Outer Space,* stated:

"Much has been written about space as a future theatre of war, raising such suggestions as satellite bombers, military bases on the moon, and so on. . . . For the most part, even the more sober proposals do not hold up well on close examination, or appear to be achievable at an early date. . . . In short, the earth would appear to be, after all, the best weapons carrier."

The advisers also came to realize that space activities had an impact on the climate of world opinion with respect to national strength and prestige. As the President's Science Advisory Committee stated in March, 1958: "To be strong and bold in space technology will enhance the prestige of the United States among the peoples of the world and create added confidence in our scientific, technological, industrial, and military strength."

With such emphasis on research activities as the major part of a total space program, building NASA around the already established NACA seemed to the Presidential advisers the natural organizational solution to the problem.

The rapidity with which the White House agreed to PSAC's proposals was due, however, to considerations other than those purely technical and nonpolitical ones which the scientific advisers had advanced. The quick action emerged from a community of interest among various elements of Congress and the Administration, since it solved several goals of Administration policy. The President, the NACA, and the Budget Bureau all favored a civilian agency. The President had consistently wished to separate the scientific or civilian from the military roles in space. As early as November, Eisenhower had made this distinction:

"If the project is designed for scientific purposes, its size and cost must be tailored to the scientific job it is going to do. . . . If the project has some ultimate defense value, its urgency for the purpose is to be judged in comparison with the probable value of competing defense projects."

No scientist challenged this view for the duration of Eisenhower's term of office. The President's position was identical to, but not necessarily a result of, the scientists' position. He agreed with the scientists because he philosophically favored civilian control in Government.

NACA's principal interest was in survival. Having reached

the point of diminishing returns in aeronautical research, NACA officials saw the space mission as an opportunity to gain larger research facilities, expanded contracting authority—and a new scientific lease on life. In mid-November, therefore, NACA launched a campaign promoting its own capacity for carrying out the Government's space effort. A special committee on space technology was appointed by NACA's chairman, Dr. James Doolittle. In a "Resolution on the Subject of Space Flight" adopted January 16, 1958, NACA outlined its work in space research since 1945, stressed that "the urgency of an adequate national program of R&D" in space was now apparent, and proposed that the national space effort could be "most rapidly, effectively, and efficiently implemented by the cooperative effort of the DOD, the NACA, the National Academy of Sciences, and the National Science Foundation," together with the nation's universities, research institutions, and industrial companies. Under this plan the National Science Foundation, in collaboration with the National Academy of Sciences, would plan scientific experiments and assign priorities for research on space phenomena for basic scientific purposes. The Foundation would financially support scientists in the detailed planning, design, and construction of special apparatus and related research.

NACA would conduct flights for scientific purposes either on its own or with Department of Defense help, in the successful pattern of airplane research programs. NACA would also coordinate and conduct research in space technology in its own laboratories and by contract in support of both military and nonmilitary projects.

Since the end of World War II, NACA had been increasingly engaged in researching the problems of space flight and had designed and constructed the special aerodynamic, structural, and propulsion facilities required for this work. For example, studies begun in 1952 led to the X-15 research rocket airplane, a cooperative project of NACA, the Air Force, and the Navy.

Finally, the powerful Bureau of the Budget under Eisenhower viewed NACA as an administratively neat solution which fitted its own special criteria. The Bureau, as a rule, did not enjoy creating new executive agencies, on the theory that current administrative resources should be used for new missions if at all possible. In Director Maurice Stan's words:

"Retrospectively, a major objective of the legislation was to build upon existing institutions and to avoid increasing the total number of Federal Agencies involved in aeronautical and space matters. . . . The bill accomplishes this aim by utilizing the NACA as the nucleus of the new agency."

Upgrading NACA also offered an efficient and economic administrative arrangement. When Killian specifically requested aid in writing the bill, the Budget Bureau set out to incorporate its favorite ideas of streamlined administrative management into this seemingly mysterious agency. Now the gears of Government moved faster.

By February 4, when Eisenhower publicly announced that a Committee of PSAC, under the chairmanship of Dr. Edward Purcell, would formulate America's future space program, the executive offices had already agreed that the new civilian space agency would be built upon NACA. Thereafter, the drafting process proceeded with an increasing sense of urgency. Public and governmental uncertainties about the management of the program were increasing, and the President was eager to send a bill to Congress to forestall independent Congressional space policy making.

Work on the legislation was done under crash conditions by the same selected group of scientific policy makers in Killian's office, NACA, and the Budget Bureau. The Bureau took overall charge of drafting the legislation, but the scientific advisers continued to participate by reviewing various drafts as they evolved. Dr. Killian had frequent contact with new Budget Director Percival Brundage, as well as direct access to the actual drafting group through a staff member, S. Paul Johnston. He also was the first agent of the administration to mobilize Congressional support for the legislation, holding several private discussions with House Majority Leader John McCormack of

Massachusetts, with whom Killian established a "heartening relationship."

The evolving administration space bill represented the common policy objectives of all the participating groups and a special blending of their particular philosophies. The final bill incorporated principles long favored by public management experts in the Budget Bureau. The drafters relied on administrative flexibility and interagency cooperation instead of setting strict boundaries around agency operations. They made the language of the bill general, since the character of the space mission was so unknown. In effect, relatively unfettered executive powers would permit the President and the Director of NASA to continue to shape the substance of the space effort.

Interagency coordination was to be routed through regular White House channels. When working level liaison and joint participation in space projects broke down, the President would resolve disputes and ultimately determine over-all national space policy.

Thus NASA emerged from these deliberations, not as an over-all national policy-making agency for outer space activities, but rather as a regular arm of the Executive Branch, specifically devoted to pursuing basic research in space sciences, operating space experiments in conjunction with other Government agencies, and cooperating with the Pentagon in R&D of military interest. These concepts were supported by the advisory scientists as logical extensions of their own basic aims. Hopefully, they would insure the President's freedom to determine the magnitude and style of the space effort.

On the other hand, the vesting of major operating authority in a single director reflected Budget Bureau management philosophy and ran counter to many of the scientists' preferences. The concept of a multimember, NACA-type executive unit composed of private citizens with professional scientific backgrounds was abandoned. Breaking sharply from the pattern established in NACA, the Atomic Energy Commission, and the National Science Foundation, the single executive structure relied on generalized administrative competence and restricted the use of a plural-member specialized body to a purely advisory role.

The proposed NASA legislation ignored specific relations between military and civilian space activities. There was enabling language included for DOD activities, but, on the assumption that these projects could be clearly delineated, no liaison mechanism was included. This principle reflected the scientists' predominant view that military potentialities of space were both "limited" and "clearly definable," as well as their belief that the military should not exercise even remote control over any of the activities of the agency. But no scientist attempted to define the "limits" of civil and military space. Thus Eisenhower remained saddled with the necessity of defending an untenable philosophy that divided space into two unrealistic realms.

The special Doolittle NACA committee on space technology, which included such scientists and engineers as Dr. Wernher von Braun, Dr. Louis Ridenour, and Dr. H. Guyford Stever, M.I.T.'s associate dean of engineering, made its report late in April of 1958. The committee recommended to NACA Director Hugh Dryden the establishment of a new National Aeronautics and Space Agency with a starting budget of $400 million— some $300 million above NACA's then current budget.

Reasonable as the administration's bill may have seemed, however, it was still nothing more than the product of a limited group of congenial interests. Other executive departments, most notably the military establishment, were not consulted during the drafting process. At this stage in the drafting, the DOD did not attempt to mold the legislation. Principally, it believed the new agency would be nothing more than a docile receptacle for scientific research projects which the military chose to entrust to it—just as NACA had been in the past. So the bill which Eisenhower finally sent to Congress on April 14 remained a compromise draft in which only Dr. Killian's office, the Budget Bureau, and NACA had participated.

What this narrowly based drafting group gained in initial unanimity, it paid for in later public criticism and conflict. Eisenhower had but few allies: the scientific community—particularly his personal scientific advisers—NACA, and the Budget Bureau.

Administration policy thus rested on a consensus that was shaky at best. Its equilibrium was soon upset by two powerful political forces—Congress and the Pentagon—both of which basically disagreed with some of the administration's space objectives and the scientists' primary assumptions. The Department of Defense mistakenly had believed that the administration bill would *not* limit its operating control over its own roles and missions. It was obviously disappointed when it saw the results in print.

Congress prepared to do battle with the administration's space proposal, but time was short. The establishment of a space agency could not wait for the two years it normally took for a piece of legislation to wind its way through the murky pitfalls of Congress, from the hopper on Capitol Hill to the President's signing in the Oval Room of the White House. This normal period would have to be at least quartered if we were to make a bold effort to catch up with the Soviets in the cosmos.

The subsequent legislative history of the space bill in the spring of 1958 is a tale of steady retreat by the scientists on several fronts. When the military realized that the administration bill would remove from its jurisdiction the original responsibility for space research and give it to NASA, it launched a barrage of stormy criticism. With the support of the Senate Preparedness Subcommittee under Lyndon Johnson, the military finally forced the administration to permit it to undertake any research and development in space which it thought had potential military relevance.

In the DOD Organization Act of 1958, a new Director of Defense Research and Engineering, Dr. Herbert York, was appointed to head the new Advanced Research Project Agency. This major change in the defense R&D structure was undertaken to give the secretary of defense a principal adviser in science and technology to supervise all the research work in the Pentagon, and to direct the centralized management of all across-the-board groups like the Directorate of Guided Missiles and the Weapons System Evaluation Group. Although "space" had been a forbidden word around the Pentagon for some months after *Sputnik,* the wraps had finally been taken off with the announcement of reorganization plans obviously in direct competition with much of the scientists' efforts. Dr. Lee DuBridge, the president of Cal Tech, warned:

"We are uncomfortably close to the situation where one of the great technical achievements in man's history, instead of stimulating vastly improved and valuable programs of real research, is being allowed to convert us into a nation of space cadets in which billions of dollars will be wasted in fanciful, fruitless and ill-conceived projects while real scientific research is neglected or even destroyed. . . . I do not believe that the conquest and occupation of the moon have the slightest military value or interest. . . . Nor do I believe that satellites floating around the earth are of the slightest use in the foreseeable future as bombing platforms. . . . There is plenty to do without trying to nail the American flag on the whole solar system by next week."

Nevertheless, against the determined opposition of DOD and the Senate, the scientists were unable to prevail to prevent the birth of ARPA as a rival to NASA.

On another front, Congress—led by Senator Johnson with the tacit approval of the Pentagon—challenged the scientists' belief that the President should have direct responsibility for policy. Congress, fearful of the administration's failure to recognize the strategic and political urgency of the space race, demanded a high-level policy-making body which would ensure a high-priority, closely coordinated military and scientific space effort.

This pressure proved irresistible. With the two houses deadlocked in late June, Johnson visited Eisenhower while Killian was in Boston. Eisenhower submitted to the majority leader and, when Dr. Killian returned, informed him that there would be a National Aeronautics and Space Council in the executive office, chaired by the President and consisting of department chiefs, among them the administrator of NASA and the secretary of defense. This group, rather than the scientists alone, would be charged with advising the President on national space policy. Johnson's nonscientific legislative assistant, Edwin Weisl, a lawyer, wrote this amendment into the administration's space bill.

Although the establishment of NASA has been viewed as a prime example of the growing influence of advisory scientists in Government, the National Aeronautics and Space Act of 1958 was the result of a confluence of forces and factors, making it difficult to estimate precisely the scientists' influence. Like the Atomic Energy Act of 12 years before, it passed Congress in a little over a half-year's time, showing that Congress could act swiftly when the national interest was at stake.

The scientists were included in the political process for the first time on a grand scale, a substantial achievement. The oldest scientific research and development organization in Government—the National Advisory Committee on Aeronautics—was also retained and expanded. Throughout the year after *Sputnik,* there was never any serious consideration by either the administration or Congress of placing space programs primarily under the military. There was, in short, no equivalent of the May-Johnson military atom-control bill for space.

On the negative side of the ledger, the scientists failed to prevail with their ideas upon the Budget Bureau when their own traditionally preferred form of organizational control through a civilian executive committee clashed with the Bureau's preference for a single administrator. The scientists' desire for a relatively low-priority, research-oriented space program also complemented the administration's need to downgrade the military exploitation of outer space for both strategic and budgetary reasons. The scientists also helped to de-emphasize the political-economic appeal of space which would have forced an open-ended expenditure of energy and resources. Finally, they served as prestigious allies for an administration clearly on the defensive.

The scientists also failed to prevail against the military. There was agreement only when their interests were congruent; for example, when the Air Force traded their former opposition to a civilian space agency in return for the lion's share of the military space mission. Similarly, the scientists failed to resist Congressional pressure for a more politically oriented space effort. In each of these situations, the administration abandoned the scientists' position to deflect potent opposition of economic and political groups without whose support the presidency could not function effectively.

Because the scientists never fully recognized the economic, military, and political relevance of space, they were only partially effective in the policy-making process. Before the launching of *Sputnik,* a pseudoscientific space effort built around the ill-fated Project *Vanguard* patently failed, as we shall see, to provide America with the technological prowess she needed to run a space race. (The one exception—our successful Minitrack satellite tracking network—was Navy operated.) After *Sputnik,* the scientific community was potent only as long as other political and economic forces had complementary objectives. When these other groups faltered, the scientists' ability to influence space policy faltered as well. Like most men in politics, the scientists were both manipulators and manipulated, members of a strategic alliance forged to serve a number of potentially gainful political ends.

But those ends were not made clear to the public for several more years—and even then, they usually took the form of a reaction to the latest Russian space advances.

# Chapter 6

# Dr. Hagen's Nightmare
# 1956-1962

The first Government space scientist to feel the sting of political infighting in Washington was Dr. John P. Hagen, the director of Project *Vanguard*. This kindly, pipe-smoking ex-Canadian had worked quietly for 20 years as head of the division of atmospheric and astrophysical research of the Naval Research Laboratory across the Potomac from bustling Washington. With his elevation to the sensitive post of director of America's first artificial earth satellite project, Hagen soon found himself over his head in administrative problems for which he had very little previous training or experience.

Our "first" space scientist was offered the *Vanguard* job after a process of elimination by the Navy. In the three hectic years he served as chief of our ill-starred *Vanguard* program, time and time again Hagen went through trying ordeals as the space age's first "fall guy." Transplanted from his quiet laboratories into an office with a dozen telephones with direct lines to the White House, the Pentagon, and Congress, the physicist-astronomer turned bureaucrat found himself exposed in a goldfish bowl from the day he assumed command.

Hagen clung stubbornly to his old habits. He continued to take his black metal workingman's lunch box, packed by his wife, to his office daily. His lunch usually consisted of a peanut butter sandwich and a thermos of milk and invariably was consumed alone. The dozen telephones included a hot line to Sherman Adams, President Eisenhower's assistant in the White House. Before *Vanguard,* the retiring scientist had only one telephone. This sudden increase of status symbols seemed to bewilder him. The pressures and hubbub in the *Vanguard* headquarters were a far cry from Hagen's earlier lab days, when no one had ever tried to speed up his slow-paced research.

What started as a purely scientific project soon became a political football. Never before had such an important scientific project been conducted under such merciless public pressure. Hagen's role as *Vanguard* chief was far different from that of his predecessor, J. Robert Oppenheimer on the *Manhattan* Project. Oppenheimer had been protected by a tight military security wall which screened him from the prying eyes of the press and the public.

Even before *Sputnik's* dramatic debut on October 4, 1957, Hagen had slowly come to realize that "the [*Vanguard*] project became an instrument of foreign policy, and then it got military overtones. We had been told to play one game but suddenly everybody else was playing by the rules of another game." He and his cohorts were woefully unprepared to play the other kind of game because no one in Washington or in the scientific community had bothered to brief him on the rules.

Hagen asked Soviet rocket expert Sergei Poloskov, who was attending an IGY meeting in Washington the day before the first *Sputnik* went into orbit, if the United States would be given time to change its radio tracking equipment if and when the Russians launched a satellite. Hagen was told that "plenty of notice" would be given.

Of course no advance word was relayed to Hagen or anyone else in America until the next day, when news of the successful orbiting of the Soviet satellite was announced to the world. Washington officialdom and the public immediately cried for action. "We need more of an S.O.B. in this program," growled one prominent Navy officer. "Somebody who will kick a few people around—someone who will raise a little hell. Hagen won't do it."

Hagen's sparse knowledge of the intricacies and technical difficulties of the *Vanguard* rocket had necessitated many postponements. He had overspecialized in his knowledge, leaving the details of planning and carrying out the program to his assistants and to the industries which participated in building the satellite rocket booster. Four times between the unveiling of the Russian *Sputnik* and March 17, 1958, when the first *Vanguard* test satellite was finally lofted into successful orbit, Hagen ascended Capitol Hill to face Congressional critics.

Twice he was called to the White House and dozens of other calls and visits to the Pentagon were demanded. President Eisenhower had personally asked him questions about the program and had even invited him, with Dr. von Braun and other members of the new scientific elite, to a special White House dinner and reception in November, 1957—the *first* such affair ever held for this professional group. (Unfortunately, this experience with the "eggheads," as they were disdainfully called, was so painful for the President that the experiment was not repeated.)

After the second Soviet *Sputnik* with the dog Laika aboard soared into space, Eisenhower increased the pressure on Hagen by his television promise to the American people that the U.S. would have a small satellite in orbit by December, 1957, and a full-sized, 22½-pound satellite successfully launched by March, 1958. Actually Hagen, after consulting with engineers of the Martin Company, the chief contractors on the rocket, had optimistically assured the President that these deadlines could be met. The many delays in the *Vanguard* program should have taught him the dangers of committing himself so rigidly.

After the spectacular explosion of *Vanguard* test vehicle No. 3 at Cape Canaveral the morning of December 6, 1957, had made mincemeat of the President's promise, Hagen found himself preparing a series of reports for the White House, Congress, and the Pentagon in an attempt to explain what had gone wrong. America needed a scapegoat, and Hagen and his fellow space scientists found themselves tagged for the unenviable role.

Prior to the *Vanguard* fiasco, no one in official Washington had ever asked Hagen to discuss our infant space science program or the satellite project. But, soon after the Cape Canaveral blunder, the scientist found himself before Senator Lyndon Johnson's Senate Preparedness Subcommittee testifying as to "why we were behind" in what had already become "the space race." He was humble enough to admit, "We scientists were at fault, really. It's like taking a woman to a ball game. If you don't bother explaining it to her you're in trouble."

After a second rocket failure and several abortions that infuriated and frustrated the usually calm Hagen, the third *Vanguard* salvaged a small portion of our lagging prestige with a near-perfect flight on St. Patrick's Day, 1958, but not before Hagen's American competitor and fellow scientist, Dr. Wernher von Braun and his team had already beaten him by putting up the *Explorer No. 1* satellite on January 31st.

A year and a half later, one of Hagen's trusted colleagues, Dr. Richard Porter, chairman of the Rocket and Satellite Panel of the National Academy of Sciences during the IGY, was grilled by the House Armed Services Committee on his role in the *Vanguard* program. He denied that he ever used improper influence in selecting his own company's engine to power the first stage of the *Vanguard* rocket. To many observers, it appeared more than coincidental that Porter, a General Electric official, had persuaded the Pentagon to pick the untried and untested G.E. engine over others.

When Porter had discovered back in 1955 that the group headed by Dr. Homer Joe Stewart, of the California Institute of Technology, was considering a G.E. engine in its deliberations on the yet-unborn *Vanguard,* he had offered to resign. According to his testimony, Stewart had persuaded him to stay on. "He expressed the view," Porter said, "that the group would want the continued benefit of my participation, and that in his opinion no prejudice would result." He noted that the Committee's 5 to 2 vote to use the G.E. engine would have carried if he had abstained.

Porter even introduced a letter from his chief in which Hagen answered columnist Drew Pearson's charges that the G.E. engine's failures—particularly in the December 6th fiasco—had put the U.S. behind the U.S.S.R. in the space race. Hagen's letter (which, unknown to the committee, had been "ghosted" for his signature by a G.E. public relations man) said that the "G.E. engine had demonstrated a degree of reliability which I believe is unequaled in American rocketry . . ."

Porter's rationale that his company's engine had performed successfully in ten of eleven launchings (even though only three *Vanguard* satellites made it to orbit) enabled the G.E. scientist to "clear the air of hearsay, innuendos and things of that kind which have been presented to this committee," in the opinion of Representative William Hess of Ohio.

But Porter did not really "clear the air" of the unasked and unanswered questions concerning the conflict of interest of an advisory scientist who helped make decisions about a sensitive project with which his own company's welfare was concerned.

In the twilight months of its existence, Project *Vanguard* was transferred first to the Advanced Research Projects Agency and then to its final resting place at NASA. After the last of the *Vanguards* went into orbit in September, 1959, the project team was broken up, and Dr. Hagen was boosted upstairs in the NASA hierarchy (at almost double his former salary) to a new post called the Office of the U.N. Conference. In this capacity, he headed plans for a multimillion dollar exhibit of U.S. scientific satellite accomplishments that was to have been shown at Geneva in 1961. But, because of Soviet recalcitrance, the Swiss space conclave was never held. Hagen was then shifted to an inconspicuous post in NASA to wait out his retirement from Government service.

After being promoted in the NASA hierarchy to two high sounding but meaningless posts away from the operational chain-of-command type of role that he played on the ill-fated Project *Vanguard,* Hagen—a now-frustrated scientist—quietly tendered his resignation in December, 1962, after more than two decades in Government service. He accepted a position as head of a new department of astronomy at Pennsylvania State University, where he was far removed from the Washington political wars that had led to his executive demise, instead of anticipated glory.

Hagen wasn't the only space scientist to experience personal nightmares after October 4, 1957, however. For a year and a half after *Sputnik,* no one in the American science community openly questioned the growing costs or purposes of our space-missile program. But several space scientists awoke abruptly from their nightmares in late March, 1959, at a conference at the California Institute of Technology in Pasadena, California. This marked the first sign of a lack of unanimity within the nation's scientific ranks about our plunge into space.

The late Dr. Louis J. Ridenour, Jr., assistant general manager for research and development at Lockheed, was just concluding a sarcastic speech in which he said that America's missile program was following America's "traditional economy of waste."

"We turn in our cars before they are worn out, and our nation would go broke if we didn't," he said. "Our missile program fits into the system very well. We send up the missiles that never come back and so we have to make more missiles. This is fine. It creates jobs and keeps money in circulation. In the not too distant future, man will be boarding the other fellow's satellites and destroying them," he concluded. "This means more satellites must be built, and the economy is kept functioning at top speed. . . ."

At this moment, a bearded scientist in a bright pea-green sports coat and black slacks jumped to his feet in the back of the auditorium. He shouted: "Our missile program is the swan song of a dying civilization!" This remark of Dr. A. R. J. Grosch, manager of space programs for International Business Machines threw the conference into an uproar.

"We don't need better missiles to destroy each other," he shouted. "The ones we have now will do the job adequately. And there isn't any point in zooming off into outer space. We could spend the money better solving problems at home—taking care of our overcrowded, underfed millions. If we did that, we wouldn't need to find new worlds to colonize."

Grosch, later elected a Fellow of the American Rocket Society (the space scientists' professional organization), continued: "We are planning to spend millions of dollars a year on new missiles and space probes, and I ask why? Why must we continue to shovel these millions into companies that are interested primarily not in new scientific knowledge but in their 7 per cent profit? That 7 per cent would go a long way toward solving the social problems that create warfare and make space exploration and colonization a necessity.

"We are in a bad way, I'm afraid," Grosch concluded, "when we try to solve our problems by mass killing—or by paddling off to a bigger island in space!"

His outburst brought other scientists in the audience to their feet, and the meeting soon broke up. Grosch's superior at the International Business Machines Corporation immediately issued a statement as a protective cover-up for his subordinate's "intemperate" remarks. He said that Grosch was only expressing his "personal opinion" and was "not speaking for the company." Obviously this scientist was not an "organization man," and he soon quietly left the company.

This episode clearly pointed out to the public that not *all* of our scientists had unanimously endorsed the national space efforts. Drs. Hagen, Ridenour, and Grosch were only three of the thousands of a new breed of space scientists who had suddenly found themselves thrust onto pedestals of public acclaim, distinction and, in some cases, notoriety. Many did not relish being moved from the narrow confines of science for science's sake. The scientists' inability to agree on how best to grapple with the complex problems of the space age was a reflection of their—and our—fears and doubts.

Their stumbling attempts to broaden their outlook to the new and wider fields of economics and politics also provided vivid testimony of the scientists' inability to understand the social impact of their work. Many other scientists, unwilling to give up their old parochial attitudes, were often severely hampered in attempting to adjust to the world of politics.

# Chapter 7

# M.I.T. Moves to the Potomac
# 1961-1963

The first three Presidential advisers all came from the banks of the Charles River in Cambridge, Massachusetts. From Harvard came Dr. George Kistiakowsky, who served from 1959 to 1961. From the austere temple of science and engineering, M.I.T., came Dr. James R. Killian (1957–1959) and Dr. Jerome Wiesner (1961–    ). Each member of this trio of scientific giants left a distinctive mark on the nation's capital during a few short years of service as special assistant to the President for science and technology.

Their influence on the banks of the Potomac would not have been so significant without the support and help provided by PSAC. When President Eisenhower created the President's Science Advisory Committee in 1957 to assist his newly appointed Special Assistant for Science and Technology, little did he realize that this small group would play such a key role in the future. One of the first things PSAC accomplished was the establishment in 1959 of a Federal Council on Science and Technology representing the top policy makers from all Government departments with significant scientific programs. The council, which included the director of R&D from the DOD and the chairman of the AEC, was set up to provide more effective intellectual cross-fertilization and cooperation within the Government.

In the early days of its existence the highhanded attitude of PSAC alienated Congress, which then sought scientific advice from "outsiders" like Teller and Lawrence. PSAC finally won the respect of Congress in 1960, when it took a less prescient approach to the major technical problems of the day. With amazing tact and humility Dr. Killian was able to end the three-sided internecine warfare which had begun to develop among the Pentagon, Senator Johnson, the Democratic majority leader, and the President's other science advisers, as to just what was the right road for science to take.

PSAC today consists of 16 permanent members, plus its chairman, the President's science adviser. Also advising the body are four consultants-at-large, including Dr. Killian, Dr. Rabi, and Edwin Land, inventor of the Polaroid camera.

While correcting some of the post-*Sputnik* Government scientific inadequacies, the Senate Subcommittee on National Policy Machinery described the successful beginnings of PSAC in these complimentary terms in June 1961:

"The President's science advisers have made themselves useful to their chief in many ways:

"They have been a scientific fire brigade. Two examples: At the outset they helped to fill a vacuum created by the lack of a sufficiently strong research and development staff within the Office of the Secretary of Defense, and they still concern themselves with a broad range of military technology. They have also helped offset the failure of the Department of State to secure technical competence adequate for dealing with such problems as arms control, nuclear test cessation, international scientific cooperation, NATO technical problems, and the like. . . .

"They have assisted the President in coordinating important programs cutting across departmental lines. Atmospheric sciences provide an illustration. . . .

"They have served the President as technical auditors of certain on-going agency programs. Their counsel has been given on project-starting and project-killing."

The present PSAC panel is heavily weighted with distinguished physics and chemistry professors from the nation's leading institutions of higher scientific learning. While most of the PSAC members are relatively nameless as far as the public and official Washington are concerned, Chairman J. B. Wiesner, who wears several hats—including that of the President's science adviser—has been continually in the limelight.

Forty-seven-year-old Dr. Jerome Bert Wiesner has been characterized (by his predecessor, Dr. James Killian) as "an innovator . . . who is always throwing up ideas . . . and using his gifts as a first rate engineer-scientist." Wiesner has never been noted as a top-flight administrator, either at M.I.T. or in Washington. During the fifties, Wiesner served for a while on President Eisenhower's Science Advisory Committee. But his first love was M.I.T. where he headed the Research Laboratory of Electronics and the Department of Engineering. The scientist met Senator Kennedy during one of the latter's presidential campaign visits to Boston. The two became intimately associated, and Wiesner worked closely with JFK's speech writers on disarmament, defense, and related issues. After the Democratic victory, Kennedy asked Wiesner to join his new Administration.

Dr. Jerrold Zacharias, a well-known physics professor at M.I.T., who advised Wiesner both in Cambridge and—as a member of PSAC—in Washington, said of his quiet-spoken protégé: "Senator Kennedy couldn't have found a better man to fill his needs. Their styles were so similar, both were young, tireless and tough minded, and both went to the heart of a situation with automatic speed." Wiesner also had an excellent background in technical military knowledge of bombs, rockets, submarines, and radar dating back to World War II. As head of Project *Cadillac,* he advanced America's military radar system to the point where we were able to detect low-flying Japanese kamikaze planes in the Pacific.

Wiesner had been dealing with military research problems for sixteen years when he first met Kennedy. He had always been noted for his social concern over the implications of arms control. From his study of the arms themselves, he had come to the conclusion that arms alone could not guarantee our security, a philosophy shared by several other leading scientists. He never felt that he underwent a conversion, but rather he decided that he could use his military knowledge to help get an arms control agreement.

Disarmament, however, had come to mean softness or appeasement and was looked upon as unrealistic by its detractors. Wiesner worried that his past disarmament activities, as a Government delegate and private citizen, might hurt the new administration, and he hesitated about accepting the President-elect's offer. After the young President-elect told Wiesner that he planned to establish an Arms Control and Disarmament Agency soon after taking office, the scientist finally accepted the offer and moved to Washington to assume his new position as Special Assistant to the President for Science and Technology.

In the evolutionary steps in science's invasion of the White House, the initial effort of the Office of the Special Assistant for Science and Technology was largely one of providing policy assistance and guidance to the President in the areas where technology impinged on national policy and security matters. In the post-*Sputnik* years it became evident that there was, in addition, a great need for a responsible group to evaluate and coordinate the large and rapidly growing Government scientific projects.

In mid-1961, a subcommittee of the Senate Committee on Government Operations, headed by Democratic Senator Henry "Scoop" Jackson of Washington, studied the management aspects of the research and development activities of the Federal government and concluded that there was a rather serious need for more intensive and extensive coordination to avoid duplication. As a result of this study, the subcommittee recommended that the Office of Science and Technology carry out this task immediately. Thereupon, OST assumed the responsibility for this activity, in addition to its primary function of advising the President.

Strangely enough, the Jackson report did not discuss the National Science Foundation, but inferred that many of its duties could be shifted to Wiesner's executive office, leaving NSF to expand its activities in gathering and analyzing information about the nation's needs in science. The report also stated: (1) that the State Department did not have a satisfactory level of technical "in-house" competence; and (2) that the foreign aid agencies had been tardy in taking advantage of the contributions which applied science and technology could make to their planning and operation.

The Jackson report on "Organizing for National Security," issued in June, 1961, also suggested some constructive means for improving the science organization at the summit of our Government. The Senate subcommittee headed by Senator Jackson had undertaken its study because of the threat *Sputnik* posed to our free institutions. The subcommittee interviewed 50 top scientists in the Government and came to the conclusion that science should *not* be jammed into one Department of Science. Therefore, the problem of organizing and directing the national science effort could not be dealt with entirely at one blow.

The report stated that the scientists' advice might not be entirely free of the "human tendency to allow their beliefs to color their technical judgments," but then continued that the President could still benefit from their advice, as he needs to see science develop "in the round, from government-wide, rather than a department-wide perspective."

Although Jackson complimented the PSAC (under Wiesner), his committee's report noted that "the science advisers have not yet done enough in helping the President and the Bureau of the Budget coordinate and monitor major government technical problems." Instead, the President and Budget Bureau have to "now turn chiefly to the departments themselves in seeking technical counsel." The report noted that the "balance of bureaucratic power is weighted heavily against a federal [PSAC] council to cut across agency lines." The report further points out that PSAC was limited in its scope because the members served only part time (with the exception of the chairman) and both they and the small staff of assistants in the OST had been too hard pressed.

The inability of Wiesner to testify before Congress (because of the custom of "Executive Immunity"), even though he was the *only* Government official concerned with the full range of *all* Government scientific and technical programs, worried Senator Jackson. He felt that the scientists advising the President should also be accessible to Congress so that Congressmen would be as well informed as the President. Consequently, he recommended that a permanent OST be set up in the Executive Office of the President, where members would be available for questioning by Congress, instead of being cloaked by Executive privilege in the White House itself.

Senator Jackson's recommendations to upgrade the status of OST were studied at length by the White House staff, and Dr. Wiesner. President Kennedy agreed with the plan and submitted the proposals to Congress in his reorganization act which established the new office March 29, 1962.

Dr. Wiesner told a House Subcommittee on Military Operations in mid-1962, "This new OST will be engaged in the two collateral activities: *science in policy* on the one hand and *policy in science* on the other."

Some Congressmen were not convinced that this move was in the national interest. During a House Appropriations Committee hearing held in July, 1962, to approve the White House request for $850,000 to run Dr. Wiesner's office (which covered a staff of 35 plus 65 part-time consultants), Republican Representative Charles Jonas of North Carolina balked. In hope of preventing the growth of a large Federal bureaucracy in this new area, he said to his fellow Congressmen: "I want him to have an adviser, and I think he needs one." Then turning to Wiesner he remonstrated: "I do not think you need 35 or 42 or 100 people down there to help you advise the President. I think he [the President] needs you and an assistant and two or three secretaries but not another research organization. I think we have plenty of those."

Wiesner, somewhat taken aback at this remark, apologetically answered: "I am not bright enough to know about everything—this is a pretty big and broad operation, and I need both staff people who have a general knowledge and knowledge of the specialized areas." Jonas and other Congressmen feared that the OST, which increased its budget from $537,000 in 1962 to a figure half as large again in 1963, might become another Government monster. But they were overruled, and Wiesner and the White House eventually got their full appropriation, when the Senate confirmed his nomination to the new post without any significant opposition.

Wiesner and his 28 aides occupy a corner of the second floor in the old State Department building just 20 yards from the White House. They share the building with other members of the President's executive staff. They moved out of the Executive Mansion in July, 1962.

Wiesner and his small group of assistants often call upon a wide variety of organizations for help in rendering the proper advice and influence in the annual Federal expenditure of $15 billion for scientific undertakings.

Wiesner sees his assignment as one of trying to give the President the proper perspective on scientific issues and to relate technical questions to policy considerations in such a way that President Kennedy will feel capable of passing on their merits. His primary job is a broad one of sorting and assessing conflicting opinions for the White House, avoiding the "mission bias" which so often pervades Government agencies.

He is often called upon to render judgment on a complex problem at a much faster pace than he was accustomed to back on the university campus. Normally, it would have taken at least a year to fully test and evaluate the 1962 Soviet proposals for the unmanned "black-box" seismic stations to take the place of on-site nuclear test inspections. But an immediate response was needed to pass on to the American test-ban delegates at Geneva. Diplomacy and politics usually cannot wait for the slow pace of science.

This sort of problem calls for the temporary bypassing of the scientific method for what Wiesner calls "a flash of intuition." "Even if the wisest Nobel Laureate in physics were

President," Wiesner has said, "he would have to fall back on intuition. Some problems are just too complicated for rational, logical solutions. They admit of insights, not answers."

The taciturn, dark-thatched science adviser meets regularly with Secretary of Defense Robert S. McNamara and the scientific assistants from each of the three services. Wiesner is looked upon as a gadfly at these get-togethers in which he never stops asking tough-minded, penetrating questions, often ranging beyond the immediate scientific problems at issue. A decade ago, Wiesner was alarmed at the general backwardness of our military technology. Now he has to watch constantly to see if the pendulum has not swung in the opposite direction. He must be alert for such a glamorous project as a plan to land an army on the moon! (He felt that this was too far out for the nation's welfare.)

Wiesner, through his representative on the President's Civilian Technology Panel, also is constantly seeking ways to probe the soft spots in the economy; buttress sick industries like the railroads; explore the possibilities of building new satellite cities throughout the country; and stimulate new industries like electronics and communications.

The importance of this area of his work was dramatized when Democratic Senator Joseph Clark of Pennsylvania in July, 1962, asked Wiesner for his views concerning "a *policy* matter with which you will have to cope"—namely, the impact of Government research and development contracts on the economic life of various communities in the United States. The astute patrician Senator pointed out that most of this kind of work went initially to Cambridge, Massachusetts, and to California, "which tended to give those two areas the lion's share of the R&D grants."

After pointing out that Wiesner would be the coordinator of many of these contracts from now on (if and when the Senate confirmed his nomination for the permanent director of the OST), Clark said, "It is wise to diffuse to a substantially greater extent than at present the geographical distribution of these different scientific activities." He stressed the fact that his own state of Pennsylvania, along with Michigan and others, was making a strenuous effort to get more research contracts.

Wiesner, formerly from Michigan, but who obviously was subjectively influenced by his more recent association with M.I.T. at Cambridge, gave an all-purpose answer in which he granted the necessity of taking this problem into account more often in the future when deciding on the location of new R&D facilities. But he hastened to add that the growth of technical industry requires the existence of adequate academic facilities in the area. He felt it was up to the local communities to provide the proper scientific and academic environment *first,* before R&D facilities were located there.

He recognized that to accomplish this primary task "we might want to provide additional supplementary funds for area development."

Clark, however, was not satisfied. It seemed to him that this was "like the question of which came first—the chicken or the egg." He was concerned with the growing dilemma caused by the concentration of technical excellence in a few geographic areas. "Perhaps I am exaggerating," Senator Clark said, "but let us assume that California and Massachusetts have a near-monopoly of technical knowledge in certain fields. Is it not a legitimate goal of prime national policy to spread technical knowledge about among the people?"

Wiesner agreed that the Midwest, in particular, had suffered during the last decade because there were too few research opportunities opening up there to keep professionals from moving away. After pointing to what had recently been done in Texas (with the establishment of NASA's Manned Spaceflight Center at Houston), Wiesner concluded: "It is a very real problem. I think it is a problem that the Federal government should help to correct. However, it does require very active support and participation by the local groups." (He didn't have to remind the Senators present at the hearing that the choice of Houston as the locale for the new $60 million space center was not determined by "local" group support, but through the direct influence of Vice-President Lyndon Johnson, chairman of the President's Space Council—and a Texan.)

In pursuit of his multifaceted politico-scientific mission, the pipe-smoking Wiesner may be in and out of the President's office three or four times a day. He has conferred with Kennedy at the edge of the White House pool, while hitching a ride in the Presidential jet, or over the radio-telephone in his chauffeur-driven Government limousine.

Although his advice is sought by the White House and high administration officials many times a day, it is not always acted upon. But the temporary setbacks don't seem to upset him, since he realizes that science is only one of many complex factors shaping the international scene. Each day he has to shuttle across the mythical borderline that separates science from politics. He realizes that technical data can help our nation's leaders to make a crucial decision—only up to a certain point. Beyond this point, they are on their own.

The success of the special assistant has been due both to the caliber of men chosen to fill this position, and to the relationship established between this office and the scientific community. It is this confidential relationship which enhances the special assistant's value to the President in the formulation and execution of public policy.

When asked on a recent television program what would prevent a future uninformed President from choosing a bad or dangerous science adviser, Wiesner answered: "Nothing. But— there would be a check on a bad science adviser by the other science advisers, in the PSAC, FCST [Federal Council on Science and Technology] and from the universities." Then he added: "The hope of democracy lies in the science adviser's judgment and vision of what the future holds."

# Chapter 8

# Technology Creeps into Foggy Bottom
# 1957-1963

For 173 years, our State Department managed to avoid a marriage with science. As long as our statesmen resided in their ugly brownstone bachelor quarters next door to the White House, they had been able to ignore every proffered opportunity to meet fair Science under properly chaperoned circumstances. The explosion of the atomic bomb in 1945 forced the diplomats to introduce themselves to the scientists. This confrontation sparked a cautious courtship of several years' duration.

The electrifying impact of *Sputnik* led to a union of these two partners despite the initial reluctance of the bridegroom, Secretary of State John Foster Dulles, to go through with the ceremony. By this time, the State Department had moved to its present domicile, a modern white building in a section of Washington known as Foggy Bottom because it borders the low swampy banks of the Potomac.

The wedding announcement appeared in the shocking disclosures made by Undersecretary of State Livingston Merchant before the House Space Committee on January 18, 1960. His testimony marked the first admission from anyone in our State Department that America was taking a severe prestige beating abroad from the adverse impact of our scientific defeats in space by the Russians.*

After World War II, the tradition-bound State Department

* The details of these post-*Sputnik* blows to the American image are more fully documented in my earlier book, *The Space Race*, Chilton Books, 1962.

attempted to have its own staff handle all atomic matters. The Department felt no need to have even a single technically trained person on the payroll. The first scientifically trained men were introduced into our Foreign Service in 1947, when 12 scientists began a short two-year tour of duty on the American Embassy staff in London. Their duties were not clearly delineated, and there was no formal line of communication between these experts and our Ambassador. The one positive result of the scientists' work was the decision to incorporate scientifically trained personnel into the State Department in the same manner as political scientists and economists before them. Yet there was still no understanding of just what the scientists would or should do once they were integrated into the diplomatic ranks.

In 1951, the first formal State Department technical program was finally established, with the appointment of Joseph B. Koepfli of the California Institute of Technology as head of the new Office of Science Adviser. He was responsible to a career man stationed below the level of Secretary of State. In addition to this new office, several embassies sprouted Science Attaché posts, which were manned mostly by men on leave from universities. During the first two years in science at State, the program failed to gain strength. Disillusioned and frustrated, Koepfli resigned in 1953. He was succeeded by an acting science adviser, who held the office for a brief period. He, too, soon resigned and was replaced by a nontechnical Foreign Service officer.

The American scientist's first modern-day skirmish with the U.S. diplomatic corps thus ended in dismal retreat. By 1955, after the various science attachés had all resigned to go back to their university posts, the experimental program was given up for dead. The State Department was demoralized from the wounds inflicted by Senator McCarthy, and, with its budget pared, there was little hope for a sudden rebirth of the diplomatic science adviser program. As one former science attaché put it: "In those days, the Foreign Service people thought you

were crazy if you openly said what you thought about Mc-
Carthy. And if you didn't tailor your reports according to
what you felt they wanted to hear back home, you were very
likely to have someone make polite suggestions to you. I didn't
want to put up with it. . . ."

However, by 1957, the State Department began having some
second thoughts about the sudden demise of the Science Advisory Office. The U.S. was becoming more deeply involved in
international scientific activities—from atomic energy to the
IGY, which began on July 1st of that year. There was a growing consensus in the higher levels of the Department that a
scientific staff was needed to assist the regular officers, not
only in their daily relations with other countries but also in
their relations with other U.S. government departments. *Sputnik*
provided the trigger for the re-establishment of the dormant
program. In early 1958, Wallace Brode, associate director of
the National Bureau of Standards, was appointed the new science adviser. At the same time, the office was elevated to the
staff level of the Secretary of State, so that it might serve a
more forceful role in policy making.

In 1960, Brode retired, and Walter Whitman, former chairman of the Department of Chemical Engineering at M.I.T., took
over the post. Scientific attachés were also sent to 12 embassies
abroad. At Foggy Bottom, politicians and statesmen had finally
realized that science is inextricably involved in public affairs
and that the research laboratory is a decisive force in the world.
The Science Advisory Office was firmly established at Foggy
Bottom.

Despite this reconciliation, the attempts to enlarge the role
of the scientists in our foreign policy deliberations were still
largely hamstrung by the bureaucratic blindness in the Department of State in the period after *Sputnik*.

Significantly, it was Congress and not the State Department
or the White House that first saw the broad implications of
science's penetration into all segments of foreign policy. On
January 5, 1959, the Foreign Relations Committee of the Senate

selected research organizations and institutions to undertake studies of America's foreign policy. Subsequently, 13 reports were published. One, the Stanford Research Report, had scientific implications.

Dr. E. Finley Carter, president of the Stanford Research Institute, and Eugene Staley, a senior international economist on his staff, were asked to undertake a study of "Possible Non-Military Scientific Developments and their Potent Impact on Foreign Policy Problems of the United States." Their report to the Senate, published in September, 1959, concluded that the progress of science and technology in the decade of the sixties would both create and help to solve foreign policy problems. The report warned that these problems would intensify unless new policy measures were taken to make a more positive use of science.

Staley and Carter pointed out that present scientific research, weighted so heavily on the side of the military, has left the civilian social applications of science far in the rear. Since our major foreign policy problems are mainly problems in human relations, the report suggested a three-point program to the Foreign Relations Committee on how we could "use science more actively for the achievement of America's international goals." Their proposals included: (1) the stimulation of additional research and development directed at important problems in the formulation and execution of foreign policy; (2) doubling or tripling the amount of basic research in fields where scientific understanding is important to foreign policy, particularly in the psychological and social sciences; and (3) the encouragement of international conferences of science and scientists in order to build bridges of understanding.

The Carter-Staley report warned our diplomats to prepare for foreseen breakthroughs based on known scientific principles. However, the authors felt that the greatest social impacts would come from new scientific principles that would lead to unpredictable discoveries. For this reason, they said, we should not try to predict social effects more than a decade ahead. In the past, they said, we had mostly erred in *underprediction* of scientific progress, especially in the space and atomic fields. Therefore, the report pointed out, our foreign policy in the future should learn a lesson from the past. We should seek new ways to aid the efforts of the people of economically underdeveloped areas to develop their resources. The authors even felt that the United States should provide leadership in establishing "The International Development Year—Science and the Underdeveloped Areas." This program would be patterned after the IGY but would obviously concentrate on helping backward nations to catch up with the twentieth century.

The Stanford report further stated that the U.S. government needed to make periodic appraisals of technological progress and to use this information in the shaping of foreign policy at an even more rapid rate in the years ahead. The report stressed the need to declassify military R&D as soon as possible in cases where such research had yielded results pertinent to peaceful civilian uses and applications—particularly in our expanding "spin-off" knowledge about commercial adaptations of atom and space products and methods.

The Stanford report also recommended that both the Foreign Relations Committee and the Executive Branch prepare a list of foreign policy problem areas where an expanded R&D program would offer beneficial results to the nation. The authors suggested such areas as: oceanography, space, food, population, communications, arms control, disarmament, and the expansion of our IGY scientific cooperation.

Establishment of a United Nations university system at the postgraduate level was also proposed in the Stanford report. Campuses would be scattered in various regions of the world, and the programs would be dedicated to the advancement of science and the humanities—with emphasis on ways to help the underdeveloped nations.

To finance this comprehensive program and to overcome the perennial money hurdle, the authors recommended that the U.N. be allowed exclusive authority to tax the use of newly discovered scientific resources not presently within the jurisdiction of any national states. "Specifically," they said, "this might mean ocean resources, polar resources, and space traffic rights." Although these areas yield little revenue at present, their future potential is enormous. (It could ultimately put an end to the annual requests to our Congress for support of U.N. bond issues to keep the world organization solvent.)

The State Department's science adviser, Dr. Wallace Brode, took issue with many of the report's findings. He recognized that changes in the financial support of our present defense programs—as compared with the smaller effort that we expend in nondefense science—would "seem to require a fundamental realignment of our national programs and policies," but he wasn't about to become embroiled in the national policy problems surrounding this explosive issue. So he paid the military a compliment for "plowing back into our culture large sums for the support of essentially nonmilitary research and development both here and abroad"—as an implied "compromise" solution to the present imbalance.

Brode also rejected the implications in the Stanford report that raising the level of the underdeveloped areas was a scientific problem. He conceded that it was mainly a "technological" problem but "certainly more of a cultural, social, and economic problem than a scientific" one. He felt that our present International Cooperation Administration's programs possessed a "reasonable" amount of science and technology.

His conservative views would not countenance the establishment of a U.N. university as recommended by the Stanford team. Brode felt that it "would not only be awkward to effect, but that there is no evidence of a demand for its formation." He felt that a more "logical" program of education could be conducted by subsidies through UNESCO.

Although Brode pointed out that our foreign science program was only modest when compared to our much larger foreign aid and mutual assistance programs, he admitted that "it becomes *important*—in a policy nature—because of the impact which science has on the foreign policy and economy of other nations." Brode didn't share Carter and Staley's concern that the State Department was *not* listed as a *major* recipient of science research funds, since he felt that his organization was *not* an operating but a coordinating and assessing agency. (He could not envisage the State Department having *more than* 25 scientists on the payroll in the future—unless the world situation changed radically.)

President Eisenhower's science adviser took a somewhat broader view than Brode in his conception of the future role of science in helping underdeveloped nations get on their feet.

Dr. Kistiakowsky described science as "the key to the future of the emerging nations" and, in this light, he said, it offers "special opportunities to us in our political approach to these nations. We have the opportunity to emphasize the importance and creativity of science in our form of society, demonstrating in terms that are meaningful to others the fruits of our technology and thus striking a more responsive chord."

The conflicting opinions of these two most influential Government science advisers resulted in no progress in the role of science on the foreign policy front during the latter days of the Eisenhower Administration. True, by January, 1960, we had quietly doubled our State Department scientific attaché staff abroad from 8 to 14 persons. Yet, significantly, some 25 nations had science attachés stationed at their embassies in Washington alone during this same period—which helped to point out the greater value many of them were placing on science, even though they were not as technologically advanced as we.

When the new Kennedy Administration assumed command in Washington, several more modest steps were taken to enhance the role of the scientists. The science adviser was elevated again by the Secretary of State to a newly established Office of International Scientific Affairs. This move upward on the ladder of our Government's foreign policy bureaucracy marked a crucial change, since it raised the science officer from an inconspicuous level of special assistant for protocol (equivalent to a bureau chief) to that of a more conspicuous Assistant Secretary of State.

The White House also gave the new office every opportunity to make itself felt throughout the State Department. When Ragnar Rollefson, former chairman of the Physics Department of the University of Wisconsin, was appointed to succeed Walter Whitman as science adviser, it was felt that a new atmosphere had been created at State that boded well for a closer liaison between the scientists and the diplomats. Rollefson's selection was looked upon as a blessing for State's science program, for he had long been familiar with the relations of science to Government, and he was respected by both American and foreign scientists. Our science attachés were gradually increased to 17 by 1962. Most of our science attachés were science department heads about to retire from their university posts. Few had any real interest in international and political affairs. It was difficult to find younger scientists willing to set their careers and research aside for a tour with the Foreign Service. Many of those who took the plunge found it difficult to adapt themselves to a life of striped-pants diplomacy.

One of those who took the plunge, Edgar L. Piret, science attaché in Paris, became a close adviser to President Kennedy's first Ambassador to France, James Gavin. Piret, former chemical engineering professor from the University of Minnesota, submitted some excellent reports to Washington on the current status of French science. These served as shining examples of the new art of scientific-diplomatic reporting.

Science Adviser Rollefson does not believe in recruiting nonscientists and giving them technical training to serve as science attachés. "It is easier to pick up politics than science," he says, pointing to the examples of Piret and our first successful science-ambassador, Benjamin Franklin, who had also served in France almost two centuries earlier.

No less an expert than Dr. George Kistiakowsky, President Eisenhower's last science adviser, disagreed with Rollefson. "Most important measure of all" is not just to attract more science and engineering graduates to regular careers in the Foreign Service, but "we must also provide a better scientific background for the nonscientists in the international affairs field," asserted Kistiakowsky.

"Scientists may well have an important role to play in the future in the policy-making process," Kistiakowsky said, "but I think it will be a different role than the one to which they have become accustomed. I think it will demand a new breed of public servant, although I am at a loss to find the appropriate name for him. The term 'political scientist' has been pre-empted for a very different use than I have in mind. I am sure none of us would want to be called 'scientific politicians,' and few indeed would dare to lay the claim to 'scientific statesmen.' But there is a significance here that is far more important than finding the right name. The role I foresee demands that this new breed of citizen-scientist must be continually aware that the scientific community must accept its appropriate share of responsibility for the intelligent resolution of the challenges facing the world." According to Kistiakowsky, America needs to push the recruitment of individuals cross-trained in both science and the added disciplines of the Foreign Service.

Dr. Killian agrees with his successor on this point. He believes that if we are to deal wisely with the application of science to foreign affairs, we must have more "scientists in government and more Foreign Service officers with scientific and engineering education who understand this new relationship." He also feels that it is important for the scientific community to recognize and give dignity to these new functions and not let public service become the haven for those scientists who cannot make a go as practicing scientists.

Some scientists, no matter how gifted, have no aptitude for public administration. Such socially minded scientists could, however, serve effectively in a foreign-policy-making capacity on some advisory committee . . . if they have the breadth of understanding to serve.

Our State Department can also make better advisory use of

the hundreds of American scientists working for our large industrial corporations throughout the world. These men have made many valuable overseas contacts and observations in recent years. Their knowledge has often helped to clarify the debates over our foreign aid program. They usually have preceded the State Department science attachés and have been able to help provide better understanding of the wisest allocation of funds by the U.S. and the U.N.

The United Nations in particular needs good scientific advice for spending its scarce money through such science-oriented agencies as the World Health Organization, the World Meteorological Organization, the Food and Agricultural Organization, and UNESCO. The disposal of U.S. food surpluses through the U.N. and the institution of food embargoes to prevent the spread of plant and animal disease from one country to another are two cases in point. Although these problems are not purely scientific ones, since they have political and economic ramifications, the proper technical assistance at the State Department level is necessary to help our policy makers to arrive at better-balanced decisions.

In time, some new term will have to be coined to properly describe these new State Department science experts. Maybe *diplotechnocrats* or *technodiplomats* might be an acceptable title to both the science attachés and the Department chiefs.

George Kistiakowsky observed recently that technological and scientific progress had acquired status as a symbol of strength in the conduct of our foreign policy. He recognized that our scientists can play an important role in international activities in the future. Just before leaving office, he raised the question of who should organize America's part in future science activities modeled after the IGY of 1957–58. He then proceeded to analyze the possible candidates for the task. The U.N.? The International Telecommunications Union? NATO? UNESCO? The International Council of Scientific Unions? Or the U.S. government on a nation-to-nation basis?

Although he offered no solution as to which—if any—of

these agencies should undertake the task, Kistiakowsky did recognize that "to integrate the scientific, political, economic, military and other factors that make up our foreign policy operations, requires, above all, competent people who understand the relation of science to these other factors."

Our "technodiplomats" or "diplotechnocrats" of the future who acquire and share this understanding will undoubtedly exert a great influence on the formulation of our foreign policy for the dynamic space age. And, who knows, one of them might even become Secretary of State some day.

# Chapter 9

# High Tide at Pugwash
# 1955-1963

Science, like music, is one of the few common languages that all men can understand. While international activities have always been part of the lifeblood of science, it is only in recent times that science has assumed a responsible political role in helping the peoples of an embittered and divided world acquire a new understanding of one another.

Since scientists are now spending more time as men of affairs, they must do more than utter pious wishes for international collaboration. They must make more specific proposals for cooperation and outline more concrete plans than they have in the past. A. V. Topchiyev, vice-president of the Soviet Academy of Sciences, recently wrote an article on this very point entitled *The Prospects of Scientific Cooperation*. He recognized that "since it came into existence, science has always been *international*. . . . The entire history of science shows that every national scientific community has only been adding its bit . . . to the great cause of scientific knowledge of the world, a cause common to all humanity."

A mutual exchange of information on national R&D programs is particularly important to prevent a duplication of effort among scientists of different countries. The recent increase in scientific knowledge (which has doubled in volume every ten years) necessitates closer international cooperation than ever before. Recently both the U.S. and the U.S.S.R. have instituted large programs of translations of scientific data into their native languages.

The many scientific agreements concerning cooperative programs and exchange of scientists that have been reached between the two governments since the IGY in 1957 are a healthy sign. The treaty signed by the world's leading powers to reserve the Antarctic for peaceful scientific research was another step toward the reduction of tension in the world.

Although these agreements provided healthy signs of international cooperation on largely scientific matters, they also foreshadowed the need for such cooperation on a far greater *political-scientific* issue—human survival on this planet. There had been a general feeling in the halls of the old League of Nations building in Geneva that the diplomats could not begin to plan for a comprehensive and complete disarmament effort until the scientists had first reached an agreement on the technical steps. So efforts were made to establish international conferences of independent scientists to discuss the problems of nuclear weapons and disarmament. Lord Bertrand Russell first fostered this idea in 1955 when he wrote an open letter to the peoples of the world expressing the conclusions developed in conversations carried out in 1953–54 between the American Federation of Atomic Scientists and the British Atomic Scientists Association. The Russell letter was signed by Albert Einstein just two days before his death. Max Born and eight other top scientists also affixed their signatures to the document.

The eleven scientists felt that their colleagues should assemble in conferences to appraise the perils of nuclear weapons. They ended their passionate plea by saying: "We have to learn to think in a new way. We have to learn to ask ourselves, not what steps can be taken to give military victory to whatever group we prefer, for there are no longer such steps; the question we have to ask ourselves is: what steps can be taken to prevent a military contest of which the issue must be disastrous to both parties. . . . There lies before us, if we choose, continued progress in happiness, knowledge, and wisdom. Shall we, instead, choose death, because we cannot forget our quarrels? . . . We urge the governments of the world to realize and to acknowledge publicly that their purposes cannot be furthered by a world war; and we urge them, consequently, to find peaceful means for the settlement of all matters of dispute between them."

The consequence of the scientists' appeal led Cyrus Eaton, a Cleveland steel industrialist, to offer his residence at Pugwash, Nova Scotia, as the site for the first Conference on Science and World Affairs (COSWA). The meetings soon became known as the "Pugwash Conferences." Of the eight COSWA meetings that have been held through 1962 (at least one a year), three were held in Canada, two in Australia, two in the United States, and one in Moscow. Interspersed with these Pugwash Conferences were the continuing multigovernment-sponsored international conferences held at Geneva on the various problems of peace.

In the fall of 1958, Dr. Jerome Wiesner went to Geneva as technical director of a sixty-man United States delegation to the Conference on the Prevention of Surprise Attack. The conclave was attended by representatives of nine other powers, including the Soviet Union. Although the conference failed to reach agreement over the issue of the best method to outlaw a nuclear Pearl Harbor, Jerome Wiesner made some valuable contacts with the Russian delegates and dredged up some solid information on the technical aspects of surprise attack.

Previously, in the spring of 1958, Wiesner met, in secrecy, with a group of the President's Scientific Advisory Committee to work out the details of an international pact to end the testing of missiles. Although their aim was narrow and their proposal also failed to hold up under political realities, much groundwork was laid for an eventual first step toward disarmament. At that time, the Soviets had a clear lead over us in ballistics missiles. Any test moratorium would have made us look weak in the eyes of the rest of the world and would have been another humiliating rebuff for President Eisenhower.

In 1959, Wiesner returned to Washington as the chairman of a twelve-man PSAC committee on arms control. The international conferences thus far had shown that our delegations had not had adequate preparation for carrying out their part in the discussions. So Wiesner and his panel met over the next five months to build up a fund of knowledge that was later passed on to the new Arms Control and Disarmament Agency, which was set up in September, 1961.

The panel made periodic secret reports to the President on the problems of international law, international armies, disarmament theories, weapon inspection, and arms reduction. Wiesner said later that "the important thing was that President Eisenhower saw fit to have the panel organized. The government was saying, in effect, that the issue of disarmament was here to stay."

Since the first of the test ban talks in Geneva in the fall of 1958, the nuclear scientists have been required to serve as negotiators and participate in the affairs of world diplomacy—whether they wanted to or not. In 1959, efforts were made by the U.S. to secure a reappraisal by the Soviets of the "Geneva System" devised by the Conference of Experts. This system was based on a world-wide network of detection stations with seismic equipment.

Other smaller disarmament conferences were held between 1959 and 1961. Most of them proved disappointing, as far as progress in the discussions was concerned, but the negotiations went on nevertheless.

Meanwhile in the seventh and eighth Pugwash Conferences held at Stowe, Vermont, on September 5 and 6, 1961, scientists from both the East and West recommended a specific program for cooperative space exploration to be undertaken immediately. Khrushchev's follow-up letter, written in early 1962, expressed his willingness to enter into a space exploration pool. This suggested that Soviet scientific leaders had convinced the Kremlin of the desirability of such international cooperation.

The Pugwash scientists' meeting at Stowe also recognized the need for the establishment of an international science center (located in a city like Berlin). Such a center could build the unique instruments for the physiological and biological studies too costly and difficult for an individual or small group of nations to undertake alone. The proposed science center could also provide help to the underdeveloped nations in the field of preventive medicine.

The twenty scientists from the U.S. and the eleven Russian delegates who participated were impressed by the serious, non-propaganda nature of the sessions. Although Senator Thomas Dodd of Connecticut attacked the conference through his Senate Subcommittee on Internal Security, it did not affect the opinions of those who were close to the Pugwash Conference. The meeting strengthened the scientists' belief that they could become a powerful influence for a stable peace if they could expand their cooperative efforts.

The conference ended with the announcement of a new "Charter for International Cooperation." The Pugwash scientists hoped that both the U.N. and their respective governments would pay heed to this charter. They all recognized the use of science for war or peace as the crucial problem of the contemporary world.

Storm clouds hung over the conference in the form of worsening political relations around the globe from Cuba to Berlin. But the remarkable progress made by the working groups— on such diverse topics as nuclear production, weapon delivery systems, and steps for disarmament—was a symbol of the success of quiet deliberations.

The more recent Pugwash Conferences have turned their attention to the broader issues, i.e., international cooperation in scientific research and rational exploitation of the world's resources, and it is hoped that they will continue to serve as prime examples of the will of the scientists to help solve world problems, despite the obstacles of international politics. The Pugwash Conferences have proved that scientists on both sides can meet together independently of their governments to discuss problems of mutual security and arms control—objectively.

Besides the unofficial Pugwash and the official Geneva scientific conferences, there has been a quiet expansion of cooperation between the United States and various foreign governments. U.S. cooperation with the European Atomic Energy Community (EURATOM) in two major programs—one for the construction of power reactors, the other for research and development related to the power projects accepted under a joint power program—is expected to be of increasing significance to the emergence of nuclear power in Europe. The recently established CERN project (the European Center for Nuclear Research) was a direct outgrowth of this idea. Our technical exchanges with the European Nuclear Energy Agency are certainly of great importance to ourselves and our partners. On a more modest scale, the U.S. has encouraged certain regional cooperation among the Latin American countries through the Inter-American Nuclear Energy Commission of the Organization of American States.

Dr. I. I. Rabi, who has made so many useful suggestions for the peaceful uses of science, recently proposed that we open one of our major American research centers to scientists from many lands, especially those from the Western Hemisphere. If a practical way could be found soon to put his idea into effect, such an international laboratory could advance the progress of science and strengthen the ties which undergird the Western Hemisphere.

There are still great impediments to achieving the potential benefits of open and complete cooperation in world-wide scientific development. The East and West continue to disagree as to the virtues of openness. But even here, the scientists have met with encouraging progress, for the International Atomic Energy Agency has provided a meeting place for the great majority of nations interested in the problems and promises of nuclear energy. Scientists in this forum have discussed and even taken steps toward the solution of such problems as the proper methods and standards for disposal of radioactive waste, safeguarding nuclear materials against diversion to military use, and negotiation and adoption of liability conventions indemnifying against harm from nuclear accidents. However, progress is slow and often beset with difficulties and conflicts.

The International Atomic Energy Agency has organized a remarkably competent staff under the inspired leadership of Sigvard Edlund. The agency has produced valuable studies of the nuclear energy needs of member states and recommended ways of meeting those needs. The prospects are that the agency will take a more active role in encouraging nuclear power development among member states.

Beyond their cooperative work in the International Atomic Energy Agency, the nations of the East and West have made some limited assaults on the communications barriers that separate them. The United States and the Union of Soviet Socialist Republics have been able to identify certain areas of mutual interest in nuclear science and technology and have engaged in exchanges of information and visits. Both nations have discussed the possibility of cooperating in an international project—the construction of a very high energy particle accelerator too expensive to be readily undertaken by one nation.

During the height of the Cuban missile crisis in October, 1962, some two dozen prominent citizens from the United States and the Soviet Union met for a seven-day session at a small New England preparatory school in Andover, Maine, to see if knowledgeable people from both countries could talk calmly about the explosive issues that separated their nations. The first conference of this type had been held at Dartmouth College in October, 1960, and the second in the Crimea in May, 1961. Both of these earlier meetings had been successful in clarification of the opposing positions, willingness of the participants to submit to discussion rules of order, and development of personal relationships.

Participants included scientists, journalists, college professors, and lawyers. They discovered at the first two conferences that the process of coming together informally and unofficially made it possible for them to engage in a full and intimate discussion that had otherwise only rarely been possible under more formal circumstances.

Neither the Dartmouth nor the Crimea meeting took place under such unsettling conditions as the Cuban crisis. The delegates from both groups watched somberly as the President announced on television his blockade of Cuba. Later in the evening, the American and Soviet delegates wondered whether to continue the conference or pack up and go home. When Academician E. K. Fedorov, chief of the Main Directorate of the Soviet Hydrometeorological Service and co-chairman of the conference, asked the Americans tactfully if they wished to go on with the discussion of their mutual problems, he noted that without a moment's hesitation every American hand in the room went up. Those of his own Russian delegation followed.

Topics for discussion ranged from the role of the U.N. in dealing with international tensions to the best ways to attain general and complete disarmament under ironclad safeguards. The most interesting and paradoxical development of the experiment was the way in which the delegates drew closer together personally as the Cuban crisis worsened and the issues that separated their nations grew more intense. The personal rapport that developed around the conference table was in evidence by the end of the week when the original awkwardness in posing sensitive questions had disappeared.

The participants seemed to sense that they were sharing a privileged experience at a critical time. The give-and-take at the conference between the Americans and the Russians increased the scientists' sense of responsibility for proclaiming personal or national views, as well as for critical self-examination.

The success of this conference was a test of the merits of the people-to-people program supported by the U.S. government. Work under extreme pressure convinced the delegates that this informal experiment should be continued to explore the continuing problems that plague mankind.

The personal relationships that many American scientists

have established since *Sputnik* with Soviet scientists, who form a major portion of Russia's intellectual elite, "can provide a bridge between our cultures and perhaps bring about a gradual erosion of the militant aspects of the Communist ideology," Dr. George Kistiakowsky said recently.

Despite the progress made by these little publicized cooperative scientific efforts throughout the world, the overriding issue of reaching an agreement on disarmament still remains unsolved. Sir John Cockcroft, a British physicist who cooperated in the world's first atomic fission experiment in 1932, in 1962 urged his fellow scientists to use their skills for solving the technical problems of disarmament. "Furthermore," said this president of the British Association for the Advancement of Science, "we must realize, however, that the great difficulties in achieving disarmament are *political* and *not technical,* and if there was a real will on the part of all major Powers to disarm, it could be achieved, releasing enormous resources for the diversion to urgent needs in our own country and less fortunate countries."

His statement does not contradict the belief, held by most scientists and diplomats at Geneva, that the technical steps first have to be submitted and agreed upon *before* the politicians can debate their merits. Dr. Wiesner feels that in this issue of disarmament lies the opportunity for the scientists, our nation, and the world to achieve true greatness. He admits that the achievement will not come easily, for disarmament will not be accomplished without a struggle. "It will take sweeping political action—as sweeping, in its way, as a declaration of war," he says strongly. "But I think everyone knows it's a struggle worth going on with."

Wiesner feels that too many people tend to look upon disarmament in "either-or" terms—either *total* disarmament or *no* disarmament at all. This type of thinking tends only to exaggerate the obstacles to arms control, he believes. The President's science adviser realizes that total disarmament can be achieved only in an ideal world, but he believes that a relatively disarmed world, guarded by an international police force, is possible. This alternative is preferable, he feels, to a military nuclear "accident" triggering an all-out thermonuclear conflict.

He offered a compromise alternative to the two extremes at the time he assumed his present post as presidential science adviser in early 1961. In one of his rare written statements, Dr. Wiesner spoke out strongly for a deliberate step-by-step cutback of arms. He also urged that the U.S. maintain an adequate deterrent force to keep the peace. "What is an adequate deterrent force?" he asked. He answered his own question: "Two hundred relatively secure missiles, based on independent studies . . . even in the absence of an agreement limiting force size and permissions for inspection." (Our present projected fleet of 45 *Polaris* submarines with their 720 missiles would, alone, more than *triple* Wiesner's concept of a maximum missile deterrent force.)

But world events have a habit of causing people in power, including scientists, to change their thinking on such controversial matters, and Wiesner was thinking about the problem in the more general terms of holding the line rather than a cutback of arms in a statement made a year and a half later. When queried by Republican Senator Tower of Texas in July, 1962, as to his present thinking on disarmament, Dr. Wiesner replied, "If we could freeze them [arms] at present levels and then provide adequate verification procedures so that we would know they were frozen, I believe it would be to our advantage. This is a *technical* problem that we must face in detail when we talk about it. That is, how can we ascertain that agreements are being honored?"

The nuclear test ban talks that were reconvened in Geneva during the late winter and spring of 1963 provided an opportunity for the leading nuclear power nations to make such agreements. Dr. Glenn T. Seaborg, chairman of the AEC, feels that "the efforts of the nuclear scientists [at Geneva] have helped to keep the negotiators directed toward solving the practical difficulties connected with any workable test ban agreement. It is possible that even this degree of focusing may have discouraged hasty and ill-considered agreements." He also says that "his assistance in the processes of negotiation has brought the nuclear scientist to greater maturity as an individual and has given him worthwhile new insights into the social character of the world."

As one prominent spokesman commented during the Geneva nuclear test ban talks in February, 1963, "When the scientists get the fever, they can bring tremendous pressure to bear upon their governments." Some of them have finally acquired the fever. Their rise in temperature eventually was felt in the White House.

When President Kennedy announced a moratorium on our nuclear atmospheric testing during his American University commencement address on June 10, 1963, he showed the first sign of reacting favorably to the scientists' pleas that we take the first step toward decreasing the chances of triggering an accidental war. His conciliatory move was also interpreted as a positive—though belated—reaction to our unfortunate nuclear blast in space eleven months before. (The repercussions of this nuclear explosion will be discussed in detail in Chapter 11.)

# Chapter 10

# Scientists Can Be Indecisive, Too!
# 1962-1963

Politics is not the only profession in which the art of decision making plays an important role in determining how far and fast we "move ahead." This fact has had an increasing impact on the new breed of scientist-administrator employed by the Federal government. Unlike fellow scientists in the laboratory who have few if any time schedules to meet, the professional scientist immersed in the labyrinths of Washington bureaucracy finds himself playing a far different role. In the campus or industrial laboratory, scientists could virtually let each new technological discovery determine their next decision for them, but not so in Government.

This decision-making problem has been most apparent in the constantly revised and updated time schedules which reflect our nation's frantic attempts to catch up with the Soviets in the space race.

In one significant aspect of our space program, the lack of decisiveness has seriously hurt our capacity to get a big jump on the Soviets in the cosmic Olympics. Our infant Project *Apollo* which, President Kennedy explained to the nation in May of 1961, would be the means of attaining our new national goal of putting an American on the moon during this decade, has been hampered by a series of indecisions since its birth. It took the heads of our National Aeronautics and Space Administration almost half a year to agree on a candidate to become the scientific manager of the program. Dr. Brainerd Holmes, an electrical engineer, who had made his mark with

RCA by managing the establishment of our Ballistics Missile Early Warning Project finally inherited the task.

Honest differences in technical opinions as to how best to achieve this new goal had been simmering beneath the surface of the Government for more than a year. These disagreements finally burst forth dramatically in mid-September, 1962, in the first example of an open lack of technical unity among top Government scientists involved in our burgeoning space program. Unfortunately, this eruption occurred during President Kennedy's two-day whirlwind tour of our major man-in-space installations in the South. It was soon spread before the eyes and ears of the whole world.

Our Chief Executive was inspecting the giant *Saturn* rocket which is designed to boost our astronauts to the moon. Just before his departure from the George C. Marshall Spaceflight Center in Huntsville, Alabama, he was briefed by the Center's director, Dr. Wernher von Braun, on the new lunar rendezvous technique approved just two months earlier by NASA's top officials as the best and quickest way to land a man on the moon. At the conclusion of Von Braun's explanation of his responsibility for the future success of the *Apollo* program, Dr. Jerome Wiesner, the President's science adviser, who had been standing quietly in the background, muttered, "That's no good!" in an obviously derisive voice.

This unexpected interruption led to a heated argument with Wiesner and Dr. Harold Brown, the Pentagon's director of research and engineering, lined up on one side, and Von Braun, Dr. Robert Seamans (NASA's deputy administrator), D. Brainerd Holmes (NASA's Manned Spaceflight chief), and NASA Administrator James E. Webb on the other.

After several minutes of vociferous public debate carried on in front of President Kennedy; Vice President Johnson; Sir Peter Thorneycroft, British Defense Minister; his deputy, Sir Robert Scott; and Wiesner's British equivalent, Sir Solly Zuckerman, the Chief Executive stepped into the fray by cracking a joke to break the tension over the flare-up.

But this heated exchange vividly demonstrated to our nation's leaders and our chief Allies that our so-called cold and rational scientists could also get very emotional. Finally, Dr. von Braun was impelled to openly and passionately promise the President: "We will land on the moon in this decade, and, by God, we'll do it!"

The NASA officials were deeply disturbed by Wiesner's sudden outburst, since they knew that he had been supported by his deputy, Dr. Nicholas Golovin, who only a year earlier, after an exhaustive study, had recommended the earth orbital rendezvous technique to NASA. Von Braun and other high NASA officials had favored this approach for an entire year until more recent studies had converted them to the newer technique of going to a lunar orbit with only one rocket instead of sending up two to meet around the earth. Von Braun's group was convinced that the lunar orbit plan was simpler, cheaper, and could cut up to two years off the time schedule. Golovin remained unconvinced, obviously nursing a personal bitterness over the sidetracking of his plan.

When the President next arrived at the Manned Spaceflight Center in Houston, Texas, Webb, Seamans, and Holmes gave Mr. Kennedy a further one-hour briefing on the justification for their new approach to the most costly technological gamble in our nation's history. To make sure that he would remain sold, they again informally worked over the President in his plush quarters aboard his jet transport—Air Force No. 1— while they were all en route back to Washington. In these latter two lunar orbital sales pitches, the NASA officials were uninterrupted, which was fortunate for them.

Two months later, NASA finally awarded its last major contract in the *Apollo* program by making its long-delayed announcement of the winner of the lunar excursion module (LEM) contract. In stating that Grumman Aircraft had been granted the 350 million-dollar LEM contract, NASA resolved for the time being the continued technical debate over the best way to send our first manned expedition to the moon. The award, which some observers predicted might eventually sky-rocket to more than one billion dollars, reaffirmed NASA's July, 1962, decision to go for broke with the lunar orbital rendezvous approach. Under this concept, a small two-man capsule (the LEM, soon nicknamed the "lunar bug") will detach itself from a larger three-man *Apollo* capsule in a lunar orbit and then descend to the moon. Several days later, the "bug" will take off from the lunar surface and dock with the main command module in a rendezvous operation. Then the two lunarnauts will transfer to the mother ship and all three astronauts will return to earth.

D. Brainerd Holmes was careful to point out that more than a million man-hours of some 700 outstanding scientists and engineers had gone into studies of the *Apollo* mission during 1962. The result of these studies "added to the conclusion that lunar orbit rendezvous is the preferable mode to undertake," said Holmes.

However, Webb admitted at the time that future technical developments might require the space agency to change its decision, so he left open the possibility of a return to one of the other backup proposals—using either a smaller craft in a direct ascent or an earth rendezvous flight. If this decision is ever made, it would be in the same vein as the dual approach that America pursued with its earlier precedent shattering A-bomb development program carried on simultaneously at both Hanford and Oak Ridge in the forties and with its concurrent *Atlas* and *Titan* ICBM program in the fifties.

But unlike their military predecessors, our civilian oriented NASA officials did not see fit to grant simultaneous contracts for two parallel but different approaches for getting a man to the moon. Because of the growing budgetary difficulties in the already fantastically expensive $20- to $40-billion *Apollo* program, our top space leaders felt that they could not ask for a second approach without prior Congressional or White House approval.

This program was already costing us more than one billion three hundred million dollars in fiscal 1963 alone, and took the largest single slice of the space budget.

NASA was admittedly gambling by awarding the lunar bug contract *before* we had successfully landed any unmanned *Ranger* moon probes. We still had no scientific data either radioed or televised back to earth on the composition of the lunar crust. Thus, our space engineers were unable to come up with the criteria for the proper construction of the landing legs and feet of the lunar bug, as well as its retrorocket engine configuration.

Because knowledge of the thickness of the lunar dust layer was necessary to properly determine the final configuration of the lunar bug, NASA was taking a chance by admittedly making a wild "guesstimate" on the final hardware design when they let the bug contract. Our first three *Ranger* moon probes launched during 1962 failed to send back any valuable data (although one vehicle, *Ranger IV,* did hit the backside of the moon by accident).

Meanwhile, Wiesner remained diplomatically silent about this latest maneuver in the running battle he had been carrying on with the space agency over our nation's prime scientific—and prestige-gaining—effort. During the next year, Wiesner did not openly question the soundness of NASA's decision, but appeared to be playing a waiting game until further developments took place on the space frontier. All experts concerned, including those on the other side of the technical debate, admitted that the earth orbital technique was the safer approach, while the lunar orbit method was far more dangerous and uncertain. Furthermore, NASA's opponents contended that such a lunar orbit route was technologically a dead end because of its limited value for future manned space travel and its limited potential military application for inspecting and destroying hostile satellites.

Moral support for Wiesner's and Golovin's approach was indirectly provided with the near space rendezvous of the twin

Soviet cosmonauts Nikolaev and Popovich in an earth orbit during August, 1962. One could conclude from the Soviet space feat that the Russians were most probably planning to use this approach as a stepping stone to putting their first men on the moon.

Although Wiesner was apparently convinced that there was little hope of reversing the present course to which NASA had committed the nation, he still held to the belief that the space agency was at least paying more attention to the eventual need for instituting a backup program using either the direct ascent or earth orbital techniques—or *both*—in the near future. If such a decision were ever made, the nation would for the first time be simultaneously pursuing *three* parallel programs on a major scientific project.

Wiesner felt that technologically his alternative ideas would become more feasible if the lunar orbital two-man expeditionary plans ran into any unforeseen technical bottlenecks. One thing was certain. No matter what the outcome of the continuing struggle over which way was the best way to go to the moon, the friction among our top space scientists which had erupted beneath a hot sun in Huntsville, Alabama, would remain with us for a long time to come. No longer was there complete harmony in the management of our *Apollo* program.

Wiesner's watchdog "meddling," as some space agency officials put it in their complaints, carried no responsibility. But it did signify the indirect authority of the White House. For Dr. Wiesner's new office is closer to the President—both physically and psychologically—than those of the NASA hierarchy located at the other end of Pennsylvania Avenue. The announcement made by Representative George Miller, chairman of the House Committee on Science and Astronautics, in early 1963 that his group was going to conduct a Congressional investigation on the merits of the lunar orbital approach in the *Apollo* program was a sign that Wiesner would again have his day in court before the actual attempt to launch men to the moon was undertaken.

Meanwhile, a second conflict between NASA Administrator James Webb and some of the top scientists in charge of our *Apollo* program erupted less than two months after the Huntsville dispute. In November, 1962, Webb, who had been budget director in the Truman Administration, announced that he was satisfied with the progress of our moon program. "We have not slipped our target dates," he said.

Though he and Holmes had stood together in the struggle with Wiesner over the LEM issue, Webb now found himself openly opposed and contradicted by Holmes. This brilliant, 41-year-old, aggressive electrical engineer-scientist, who had a talent for ramming through tough projects, believed that the *Apollo* program had slipped four to six months behind schedule. He blamed the lag on Webb's dragging his feet and his unwillingness to request any supplemental funds from Congress.

Webb, a businessman, irritated Holmes by saying "the moon program is important, but it is not the only important part of our space program." This brought a retort from Holmes: "I don't agree with him. I think it's the top-priority program within NASA." Project *Apollo* first ran into money trouble during the late summer of 1962 when the major contractors said the program would cost $400 million more than their original estimate. Holmes then asked Webb for additional funds of $2200 million for fiscal 1963 to keep this program and *Gemini* (its preliminary project) on schedule. Webb refused this request, since he thought that asking Congress for more money in a deficit budget year would only anger the legislators and imperil the entire space program.

"What is more," declared Webb stubbornly, "I am not willing to transfer millions of dollars from other NASA programs into manned space flight." Thus Holmes had no choice but to cut back the program.

Retrenchment came quickly. In St. Louis, McDonnell, the prime contractor on the *Mercury* and *Gemini* capsules, put strict limits on overtime work. In Baltimore, the Martin Company laid off 225 men working on the *Titan II* space booster for the two-man *Gemini* capsule. In Houston, one official at NASA's Manned Spaceflight Center gasped: "I thought we were in a race. My God, we've got guys going out of their minds trying to get things going." In Huntsville, Alabama, Von Braun pleaded: "We cannot let things slow down any more than they have."

The White House was in a dilemma. President Kennedy still wanted to get an American on the moon with the "utmost urgency," preferably before he left office. But this major gulf between Webb, as the Government administrator, and Holmes, as the scientist-manager, was a warning that the whole program might yet bog down. When the President's new space budget was announced in late January, 1963, there were no additional funds for the *Apollo*. So once again the scientists who wanted a stepped-up space program had taken a licking.

On the same day that the Russians launched their semisuccessful *Lunik IV* toward the moon (April 2, 1963), Holmes testified before a House Space Subcommittee that the Soviet space shot was no reason to change the pace of Project *Apollo*. In this reversal of his stand taken five months earlier, he acknowledged that the *Apollo* program was not "going as fast as it could be if more money was spent on it." But he then said in a subdued mood:

"In my judgment we are going at a reasonable and proper pace. I think it would be foolish to squander money on an all-out crash program, just as I think it would be a foolish thing to risk life in order to get there first." But by now Holmes was becoming thoroughly discontented with the lack of support shown by the hard-talking Webb and Congress toward our man-on-the-moon effort.

On June 12, 1963, on the eve of the record-breaking Soviet twin cosmonaut flights of Colonel Valery Bykovsky and Lieutenant Valentina Tereshkova, NASA quietly announced that Holmes was resigning to go back to industry. Holmes had become so progressively disillusioned as he watched Congress hacking away at the proposed $6.6 billion NASA budget for fiscal 1964, that he soon realized there was little chance of our beating the Russians to a rendezvous in orbit, manned circumlunar flight, or the historic lunar landing itself. He was subsequently replaced by Dr. George Mueller, a vice-president of the Space Technology Laboratories in September, 1963.

His woes were further compounded by the increasing number of brickbats being hurled at our moon efforts by distinguished American and British scientists, who made public statements that the billions could be better spent on cancer research and foreign aid. Sir Charles P. Snow, who was in America at the time, said that "America's haste to reach the moon was probably a mistake." The British scientist criticized the all-out nature of the American effort, saying that Americans were "abnormally sensitive" to Soviet space feats. He felt that we should put our efforts into exploring the more dramatic developments in molecular biology during the next decade and let our space programs progress at a more "natural pace."

Snow's "go-slow" attitude, coupled with former President Eisenhower's blistering "no-go" statement—that anyone who spent $40 billion to go to the moon was "nuts"—provided the final *coup de grâce* to Holmes's brief tenure as head of the most expensive national scientific effort in our nation's history.

Meanwhile, NASA announced that it was considering the possibility of sending a scientist along as one of the three crewmen on the first *Apollo* trip to the moon. The other two presumably would be ex-test pilots like the *Mercury* astronauts. On December 26, 1962, Homer Newell, director of space sciences for NASA, confirmed that the question was under serious consideration in Washington, but he said that no decision had yet been made as to whether the lucky candidate would be a biologist, geologist, meteorologist, astronomer, astro-physicist, or physician. Newell felt that the final decision would be made on the advice of a special scientific panel.

The NASA space science director was not going to commit himself by designating a particular field of science as the one from which our first lunarnaut should be selected.

Obviously, good lunar priority arguments could be made for each scientific discipline, so the final decision as to who will be the first American scientist on the moon will probably be both "scientific" and "political."

It would be interesting to know what criteria the Soviet Academy of Sciences is using to select their future male and female cosmonaut-scientists. Maybe their first lunarnauts will be cross-trained in several appropriate scientific disciplines—thus an answer to the somewhat pedantic American argument as to which is the *most* important science in which man should be *most* knowledgeable, when he first sets foot on the moon.

The voice of American science, calling for more active participation in our manned space efforts, was heard soon after this preliminary NASA scientist-astronaut announcement. In early January, 1963, a group of leading scientists under the auspices of the Space Science Board of the National Academy of Sciences issued *A Review of Space Research*. In this weighty study, the conferees asked the Federal government for a proper exposition of the scientific concepts of the *Apollo* moon mission to allay the misunderstandings and considerable confusion surrounding its justification.

Several of their recommendations suggested a more definite role in the manned spaceflight program for the scientific community. The scientists urged that immediate contacts be made between astronauts and astronomers for an exchange of ideas.

The scientific study group also recommended that a *meteorologist* be made a member of the crew of our future space observatories, beginning with *Gemini*. They strongly urged that scientists should participate on all future space missions—as astronauts, passengers, or ground-based observers. They suggested that the present group of "test-pilot" astronauts be given special training to qualify them for scientific observations. They wanted a biologist selected for astronaut training immediately, so that he would be available for the first Mars mission.

Finally, they suggested the early establishment of an institute of space sciences adjacent to the NASA astronaut training facility at Houston, Texas, to be administered preferably on contract by a university.

In planning the fiscal 1964 space budget, many scientific advisers and others within the administration debated the question of whether the nation could afford to spend both the billions necessary to land a manned expedition on the moon in this decade—with or without a scientist going along for the ride—and still devote hundreds of millions of dollars toward the development of a nuclear-powered rocket that would not be needed for deep space exploration until the early 1970's.

In late 1962, several influential scientific advisers close to the White House urged that the *Rover* nuclear rocket program be scaled down and held to its $200 million level instead of doubling its costs, as requested by the joint NASA-AEC project officials. The several unsuccessful test firings of the *Rover* ground-harnessed *Kiwi-B* reactor during 1962 did not help the cause of those scientists who championed this device as the best means of leapfrogging the Russians in space.

Dr. Edward Welsh, an economist who was serving in a key position as executive secretary of the National Aeronautics and Space Council, took up the cudgels against the conservative scientists who were opposing a crash program on *Rover*. On November 28, 1962, he warned that nuclear rockets would be essential for manned trips beyond the moon and that we would be confronted with a "space gap" if we did not push "enthusiastically the potential of nuclear energy and power at an increasing rate in the field of space." A short time later, he again referred to the resistance of some scientists to the increasing cost of our space program when telling a Washington luncheon audience: "There are bound to be stupid people in every field. Just because they're labeled scientists doesn't eliminate them from being stupid!"

Dr. Glenn T. Seaborg, the first scientist to serve as chairman of the Atomic Energy Commission, also saw fit recently to comment on the growing problems of Project *Rover*—now that it has become a major contender for research dollars. In frank terms he said: "Very little imagination is required to visualize the increasing pressures to which the President and Congress will be subjected as the growing financial needs of the nuclear space program are forced into intense competition for funds with other parts of the space effort, with defense requirements, and—to be realistic—with other segments of the atomic energy program, including the commission's recently recommended program for utilization of our energy resources to meet the nation's future electric generating requirements."

Seaborg concluded: "Some feel that this ultimate competitive situation is at hand; and classic arguments for a balanced economy are being heard more clearly. One senses increasing concern over our national debt limitations. It takes no crystal ball to predict that these problems will loom ever larger as funding requirements increase. Some very difficult national choices may have to be made."

Unfortunately, there did not appear to be any consensus in scientific and other high Government administration circles to cut back any of the fat in the ever-burgeoning Department of Defense. That segment of our Federal budget was considered "sacred" for the protection of the national interest. Rather, the scientists aimed their barbs at NASA *civilian* scientific projects which they felt would be politically safer for them to criticize. Most of them lacked the courage to speak out against the all-powerful military-industrial complex which guarded the financial gates of the Pentagon.

Except for a few dissident and disenchanted atomic scientists, American scientists have not attempted to rebel openly. Many have complained about the internal operation of our defense production methods. While they have hesitated to tangle openly with Pentagon officials on defense policy, the scientists of the aerospace industry have felt no qualms at venting their wrath, mainly behind the scenes, at abuses and injustices which they believe should be corrected in the interests of fair play. Foremost among these complaints was the industry-wide attack against the Ramo-Wooldridge Corporation's scientific management of the expanding military ICBM program.

After five years of increasing conflict between the scientists and engineers of industry and Ramo-Wooldridge scientists and engineers, drastic action had to be finally taken by the Government. No rapprochement was in sight, and hundreds of missiles still had to be built to fill up the underground silos being dug around the country.

The Air Force eventually had to set up in 1960 a separate Government-operated nonprofit outfit, called the Aerospace Corporation, to solve the problem. Advance planning for all new Air Force space programs was transferred to this new corporation. R-W, through its Space Technology Laboratories subsidiary, was allowed to continue supervising the ICBM-IRBM program until it was completed.

Meanwhile, the original R-W Corporation had merged with an automobile valve supply company and became known as Thompson-Ramo-Wooldridge, Inc. T-R-W soon spun off Space Technology Laboratories—as an independent subsidiary—in an attempt to ward off further complaints about the lab's being "too cozy" with the Air Force. For its advisory service to the Government, R-W was paid a handsome 14.3 per cent fee of the total cost of the contract—one of the highest ever awarded by the U.S. government. Since the combined ICBM-IRBM contract ran into the millions, this resulted in Messrs. Ramo and Wooldridge becoming millionaire scientists almost overnight.

With Space Technology Laboratories no longer tied to a purely advisory role, it has shifted over into manufacturing and has already landed some juicy prime hardware space contracts from the Government. Foremost of these is the $19 million *OGO* (Orbiting Geophysical Laboratory), a "streetcar satellite" for NASA, a hush-hush Project #823 classified Air Force spacecraft, and the new space-to-ground communications system which will form the basis of the future Air Force command system for controlling many types of military satellites simultaneously. They have also obtained large subcontract jobs on the NASA *Sunflower* satellite and the Army *Advent* communications satellite.

The prosperous STL, which is only one division of the parent T-R-W Corporation, is now doing over $100 million worth of business annually (with only $35 million of it being in the old ICBM advisory category). The lab now has forty-two customers in place of its original one—the Federal government. This lusty young space age firm with over 100 contracts and 6,000 employees is headed by a 39-year-old ex-Cal Tech scientist, Dr. Ruben Mettler.

The original founders have been able to sit back and enjoy the fruits of their labors. Wooldridge recently resigned his $100,000-a-year executive post to go back into basic research. Ramo, who is still active as a corporation vice chairman, roams the country as a combined troubleshooter, policy maker, and observer to keep his industry informed of what's coming next in the fast-changing world of technological advances.

One of these advances may be a big breakthrough whereby electricity can be generated from seawater through the action of bacteria on certain chemicals. The Navy and the Government are deeply interested in this possibility which is being explored by another T-R-W subsidiary, the Magna Corporation, under its genius president, Dr. Gibson Rohrbach. As Ramo sums it up with a quip, "Batteries, bugs, or what you will—we're in it." If Rohrback succeeds with his bold experiments, it could well revolutionize the production concepts and sources of electric power for our big coastal cities as well as for ships at sea.

And T-R-W are in it not just as *advisers* to the Government, but as their own policy makers. T-R-W has already produced many profound effects on U.S. government policy—from the depths of the ocean to the far reaches of outer space. Like the dozens of new electronics-aerospace industries and research laboratories that have sprung up in America since *Sputnik*, this enterprise has demonstrated that scientists can work indirectly with the Government without being employed directly by the Government.

This pattern of private industry-Government cooperation, particularly in the scientifically oriented space-missile field, is a new phenomenon in our country. However, only those companies that get the juicy contracts can afford to plunge ahead and build the products for which there is only *one* customer—Washington. As the economist Seymour Melman recently put it, what do the scientific-industrial managers in our aerospace industries really think when they look around them at their Government-owned facilities—where even the water coolers are U.S. property?

Fortunately, the problem of the ultimate ownership of the billions of dollars' worth of Government-owned plants and laboratories is one question which the scientists will not have to decide. That decision remains in the hands of the people and their representatives in Congress.

# Chapter 11

# The Starfish That Wouldn't Die
# 1962-1963

When natives in the tropics or tourists on a holiday discover a live starfish swimming placidly in an azure lagoon of some picturesque coral atoll, they often pluck it out of its natural habitat to take home as a decorative souvenir. But these five-pointed marine creatures have to be dried out in the sun, where they soon harden and die, before they can be useful to man.

There was one captive starfish, however, that refused to die like the rest. Strangely enough, this peculiar starfish, which happened to be man-made, defied its creators because, though it, too, was not expected to live very long after its initial contact with the atmosphere, it lived much longer than most scientific observers predicted.

What made this starfish different from the others? First of all, this monster was never intended to go near the water. It started out in life as a multimegaton hydrogen bomb nestled inside a rocket nosecone, perched on the launch pad at Johnston Island in the mid-Pacific Ocean. When it was finally born in a flashing burst of light in the middle of the night, it took the form of a familiar blossoming mushroom cloud that lit up Hawaii—hundreds of miles away—as bright as day. *Starfish* was the code name for this high-altitude experiment—one which caused a profound and prolonged controversy in scientific circles for months after it had burst out of its protective cocoon.

When the United States first announced that it planned to carry out a series of high-altitude nuclear detonations over the

Pacific in the summer of 1962, many scientists in America and abroad expressed deep concern over the possible effects of these shots on the earth's magnetic field, the outer atmosphere, and the Van Allen radiation belts. Among the most critical were several leading British scientists led by Sir Bernard Lovell, director of the famed Jodrell Bank radio telescope in Manchester. He said that the forthcoming experiment was "one of the most clumsy and dangerous experiments ever devised . . . and [would cause interference] with the environment of the earth." He framed his critique in terms of the largely unknown physical mechanisms that create and destroy the natural radiation belts. "Such an affront to the civilized world," he said, "would be a display of utter contempt for the grave moral issues involved."

Lovell went on to say: "The proposals to make nuclear explosions in space arise from a small group of [American] military scientists, unknown and unidentified to the world at large, who have persuaded their masters to make a series of huge gambles under the guise of defensive necessity. On the scale of the cosmos they are dealing with fireworks. Nevertheless the earth is so minute on the cosmic scale and its environment is controlled by the delicate balance of such great natural forces that one must view with dismay a potential interference with these processes before they are investigated by the delicate tools of the true scientists." His scientific judgment raised a widespread discussion over the moral issues involved in the proposed tests' effects.

Dr. S. Fred Singer, a noted American authority on high-altitude physics, disputed Professor Lovell and predicted that the effects would be "small and harmless" and that the earth's natural radiation belt would be only "slightly perturbed." He felt that even a "major, temporary modification of the radiation belts should not be cause for objecting to the high-altitude test," since we must then object to solar flares and magnetic storms, which cause "natural fluctuations greater than any man-made effects."

Singer justified the proposed tests on the "scientific" grounds that the modification of the trapped radiation was precisely what one needed "to determine the important properties of radiation." Yet Singer did agree with Lovell on the moral grounds that "no government had the right to change the environment in any significant way without prior international study and agreement." He felt that the advance U.S. warning was sufficient notice to the rest of the world. He further justified our planned high-altitude *Starfish* experiment by comparing our "openness" with the "secret" space launchings of the Soviets.

In late May, 1962, a SANE-sponsored group of eleven prominent American scientists, including Dr. Albert Szent-Gyorgyi, issued a signed statement urging the President to postpone all high-altitude tests until studies could be made of their effects by the newly created Consultative Group on Potentially Harmful Effects of Space Experiments. This special six-member panel was set up in May of 1962 by the Committee of Space Research of the International Council of Scientific Unions. The group of eleven scientists felt strongly that the stated scientific reasons did not justify the proposed tests.

Even the influential New York *Times* ran two editorials in the late spring of 1962 taking issue with the experiments. They stated we had no right to tamper with the belts because they "do not belong to the United States." The President and the Pentagon did not heed these warnings, and the scientists proceeded with their plans.

Many other world scientists had also expressed the opinion that the radiation belts above the earth were not ours to tinker with unilaterally. Our arrogance in not informing the world or requesting permission through the United Nations before we set out to conduct the high-altitude tests caused further doubts to be raised not only about the forthcoming tests, but over the secrecy surrounding the earlier lower-altitude nuclear shots conducted over Johnston Island by the American scientists during the IGY. These shots, which produced an artificial airglow and aurorae, when coupled with the secret Project *Argus* A-bomb tests held over the South Atlantic in August, 1958, caused many of our allies to question our real motives.

As a result of these criticisms, the United States Atomic Energy Commission and the Department of Defense, which jointly planned the tests, called together an assemblage of top U.S. scientists who were competent to analyze the problem, in order to determine if their technical concern was of sufficient stature to warrant a possible change in the detailed planning of the *Starfish* tests. The scientific assemblage concluded that "these planned U.S. explosions in the upper atmosphere will not greatly disturb conditions for the magnetic orbits of the particles in the Van Allen belt. Perturbations produced on the inner belt *will be minor if detectable at all.*" [Author's italics.]

Dr. Van Allen supported this joint AEC-Pentagon view by calling the proposed space bomb explosion "an interesting but not a dangerous experiment." President Kennedy told a press gathering in Washington late in the spring of 1962 that his advisers had assured him of "their very careful scientific deliberation" before approving the shot. He told the assembled newsmen, "Van Allen says it [the space bomb] is not going to affect the belt, and it [the belt] *is his.*" But was it Van Allen's belt, as the President assumed, or did it not belong to *all* of mankind on the earth? Did we have squatter's rights in the sky just because we discovered the belt first? The President concluded his remarks on the forthcoming space bomb test with these words: "What we are attempting to do is to find out the effects of such an explosion on our security, and we do not believe that this will adversely affect the security of any person not living in the United States."

On the following morning Professor Fred Hoyle, one of the world's most distinguished astronomers, warned in *The New Scientist,* published in London, that if a megaton nuclear bomb were exploded 500 miles above Johnston Island, the Van Allen belts might be breached with incalculable results continuing for centuries. He observed: "The morality of making what might possibly be a long-term change in our environment can very properly be questioned."

His understanding of the height of the proposed megaton blast was shared by most scientists around the world. Then on May 29, 1962, a press statement issued jointly by the Pentagon and the AEC said that there had never been any intention of exploding a megaton bomb at that elevation. The bigger one would be fired lower down with only a "sub"-megaton bomb exploded at the 500-mile level. Anyway, the scientists were convinced that the effects of the space bomb "would disappear within a few weeks to a few months," according to the press release.

On July 9, 1962, the U.S. exploded a multimegaton (equal in power to 1.4 million tons of TNT) hydrogen bomb some 250 miles above Johnston Island. The unexpected results of this AEC *Starfish* explosion created a storm of protest around the world and created havoc with the Van Allen radiation belts. William Laurence, science editor of the New York *Times,* wrote in a post-mortem column: "In the face of these confident predictions, the results . . . constitute the biggest surprise so far since the beginning of the space age." The resulting high-energy electrons that were trapped in a 3,000-mile thick radiation belt damaged five U.S. satellites, putting several (among them the *Injun, TRAAC, Transit IVB,* and the British *Ariel*) out of commission—and temporarily knocking out *Telstar*— by damaging their solar cells.

Although there had been an earlier inclination to dismiss Lovell's outburst against the shot as British "sour grapes," his worst fears were now proved correct, even though Dr. Van Allen and other American scientists calmly predicted that most of the new artificial radiation would dissipate in a year's time. But other NASA scientists predicted that the new belt would last from 10 to 100 years.

The Soviets were so worried about the possible harm from this shot to their future cosmonauts' health that they sent a special radiation detecting *Cosmos* satellite aloft in mid-July to test the effects for themselves before they risked sending Major Andreyan Nikolaev and Colonel Pavel Popovich up on their historic dual multi-day orbits in August.

Meanwhile, Dr. Wiesner and the President's Science Advisory Committee issued an "official" report on the *Starfish* tests. The report came—without warning—several days before a secret background conference on the subject, which was to be held September 10 and 11, 1962, at the NASA Goddard Spaceflight Center. The White House report—based on *Telstar*—stated that the new radiation belts were more intense and longer-lived than had originally been anticipated. Several scientists not on the committee, including Dr. James Van Allen, immediately criticized the announced results as "wrong."

Van Allen felt that PSAC's conclusions resulted from a "naïve interpretation" of the data, rather than any error in the data. Since *Telstar* probably was measuring the earth's natural radiation belt, according to Van Allen, "the committee essentially garbled the whole business, and told the world that we didn't know what we were doing." He attributed PSAC's hasty action to pressure from Government circles for the rapid release of scientific findings. In the several appearances that he had made before it, he said, he had felt "intimidated by the frenzied atmosphere."

Despite PSAC's unexpected thunderclap, NASA and the Defense Department officials were so concerned with the political implications of the *Starfish* boomerang that they went ahead and held the scheduled two-day secret briefing in mid-September for several hundred industry and government officials. They hoped to resolve conflicting opinions and to explain the scientific details of the true nature of the unexpected long-term intensification of the radiation belts around the earth. It was pointed out that the principal hazard from the high-energy electrons to unmanned spacecraft was to solar cells—such as those knocked out in the five dead satellites. The recommendation was made that all future satellites using solar cells to convert sunlight into electric power be shielded with a radiation-resistant covering called "N-on-P [for neutron-on-proton] type silicon" instead of the old "P-on-N" type of covering that was mortally damaged by the satellite-silencing *Starfish* burst.

NASA officials were so disturbed about the potential radiation effects on man that they allocated $9 million in September for a rocket booster and a special *Explorer* satellite designed to examine the intensity of the new *"Starfish* Belt" at firsthand. The official prediction of *Starfish's* performance underestimated the bomb's effects, and failed to foresee the intense radio "hiss" that appeared in the lower portions of the new artificial belt. The unpredicted effects of *Starfish* clearly demonstrated a glaring lack of scientific knowledge about space bombs. Obviously, a reliable prediction could *not* have been made in advance of the July 9th shot.

Ironically, it was the sudden termination of the sending of data from the American-launched, British-made *Ariel* satellite—three days after the blast—that gave the first clue to the world that something unexpected had occurred in the cosmos. The fading of radio signals from *Ariel* was caused by radiation damage to her solar cell devices. This tiny satellite, launched on April 26, 1962, was Britain's *first* successful artificial earth satellite and it was unfortunate that our H-bomb had to silence its useful life so soon after its orbiting.

By mid-November, Dr. Jerome Wiesner "recommended" that NASA issue no further releases on the results of the *Starfish* test until there was agreement on the interpretation of the data on the radiation belts. NASA interpreted his advice as an "order," so the NASA scientists reversed their quick release policy on all data which had a bearing on the controversy and stopped giving out any more data about *Starfish* after October 31st.

In late December, at the annual meeting of the American Association for the Advancement of Science, Van Allen again violently disagreed with the PSAC conclusion that the new artificial radiation belt was more intense and long-lived than had originally been estimated. But PSAC's report—the only *official* Government report on *Starfish*—has never been retracted!

Van Allen repeated his prediction, which he first made in May of 1962, that the decay rate of the artificial belts would leave them virtually undetectable by the summer of 1963. He based his conclusion on his analysis of the *Injun* satellite's data and said that the committee, by its opposite conclusions, was giving to the world a false impression of U.S. scientific ineptitude. The discoverer of the natural radiation belts around the earth added that PSAC had erred in going beyond the intended scope of its advisory capacity when it permitted itself to "decide what the facts are."

Van Allen then suggested the establishment of an *ad hoc* committee from the National Academy of Sciences in order to prevent a similar occurrence after any future high-altitude thermonuclear tests. Such a committee, Van Allen said, would announce all forthcoming tests, publish the theoretical predictions, and carefully analyze the resulting data before releasing any results to the public.

"The committee [PSAC]," concluded Van Allen, "possesses an air of authoritativeness inappropriate to sound judgment. They intimidate the small man against bringing forth scientific findings."

Obviously, no matter who was right about *Starfish's* life and death, the committee had, by its actions, made what amounted to official government *policy* statements when its members merely intended to make an *advisory* statement. Here was a prime example of the scientists moving away from their former purely *advisory* capacity into the controversial political sphere, either consciously or unconsciously.

Dr. James Warwick, a radio astronomer of the University of Colorado's High Altitude Observatory, concluded in December, 1962, that both "Lovell and Singer were at a standoff as far as scientific appraisal of this particular bomb test is concerned.

Lovell did not grasp the most certainly damaging phenomenon, namely the *radio astronomical effects,* and Singer chose to state his case so that the crucial question, *particle acceleration,* was entirely omitted from the argument." Warwick said the new belts only interfered with radio astronomy at low altitudes for a short period.

As an afterthought, Warwick further stirred up a tempest in scientific circles over the *Starfish* test. He postulated that if the "scientific community had asked itself coldly what experiments needed to be done, it might or might not have determined that high atmosphere explosions were desirable." Warwick thought most scientists would not have approved the tests—if they had been asked. The tests were undertaken because the final tribunal in such cases is a military-political board, rather than scientists. In his final remarks to a group of fellow scientists (including Van Allen), Warwick said, "Until it [the Government] permits the scientific community political stature from which to exert decisive weight, the United States should not rationalize its political judgment with spurious scientific arguments."

He agreed with Van Allen's charges against PSAC. Warwick said that when he first tried to deliver the results of his radio measurements of the artificial blasts, which were consistent with Van Allen's conclusions, he felt as if he were "crying in the wilderness."

*Starfish* was still very much alive. Well into 1963, a crux of disagreement still existed within scientific circles over the precise results of the July 9th nuclear test. The prolonged argument stemmed from the different ways various scientists interpreted the reports of the sensitive radiation-measuring instruments aboard the various satellites affected by the blast.

Though the PSAC status report had been also concurred in by the AEC, the Pentagon, and NASA, Van Allen criticized it. He preferred to draw his conclusions solely from the *Injun* satellite, which had a higher threshold of sensitivity than *Telstar*. But *Injun* did *not* pass into the radiation-free slot region between the inner and outer Van Allen radiation belts, as *Telstar* did. Thus *Injun's* radiation-reading capabilities were limited. (*See illustration.*)

*Telstar*—upon whose experience the PSAC report was based—was not launched until July 10th, the day immediately following the *Starfish* test! Because *Telstar* could not compare *pre*blast and *post*blast levels of radiation, it, too, had its limitations. This only further confused the true picture of what really happened on July 9th—as far as the public was concerned.

One prominent scientist, Dr. Irving Krick, who was head of the Meteorology Department of the California Institute of Technology for ten years, recently propounded a theory about the July 9th and other H-bomb explosions in space to explain why the winter of 1962–63 was one of the coldest in history. Krick, who now is president of his own weather forecasting firm, postulated that "last year [1962] we discovered that the intensity of the polar outflow from Canada was more extreme than would be anticipated. To us this meant that something was happening in the high atmosphere—the equivalent of a considerable increase in solar energy output.

"It is our view that a man-made radiation belt, formed by H-bomb explosions, is having the same effect as an increase in the output of solar radiation. This unprecedented and unexpected heat source is forcing jet streams of cold air to plunge southward from the Pole at speeds great enough to carry snow to latitudes that have seldom, if ever, experienced it."

While Dr. Francis Reichelderfer, chief of the U.S. Weather Bureau since 1939, is cool to the Krick theory, he admitted that the explosions *did* strengthen the Van Allen belts. Other scientists expressed sympathy for the idea. Dr. Wilmot Ness, chief of the Theoretical Division of the NASA-Goddard Space-

→

Artist's rendition showing "skirt of electrons" added to the lower Van Allen radiation belt as a result of the July 9, 1962, "Starfish" hydrogen space bomb blast over the Pacific Ocean.

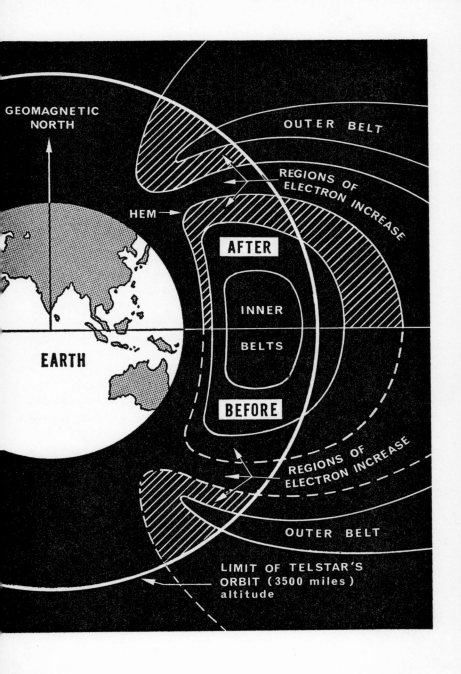

flight Center, said: "There is no doubt that a fair amount of radiation particles from H-bomb blasts goes downward and may influence the atmosphere where the weather is actually made. . . . It could be enough to trigger a weather process already building up—or even possibly modify the path of a tornado."

In mid-February, 1963, Democratic Senator John O. Pastore of Rhode Island held a special two-day briefing of his Commerce Communications Subcommittee on the successful performances of the *Telstar* and *Relay* satellites. In the course of the Senate hearings, Eugene F. O'Neill, director of the Satellite Communications Laboratory of Bell Telephone Company, predicted that there would be a second failure of *Telstar* in the near future because of radiation effects. (This satellite had previously been repaired in orbit—almost miraculously—after its first solar cell failure.)

O'Neill's boss, James E. Dingman, executive vice-president of AT&T, followed him as a witness and made the astounding statement that the radiation intensity inside *Telstar* has been a hundred times greater than anticipated when the satellite was launched into its elliptical orbit of 600 to 3,500 miles above the earth. He noted that there was a slight increase in radiation resulting from the Russian atomic explosions, which lasted for only a few days. But he gave *no* other explanation as to why the radiation exposure of *Telstar* was so many times greater than calculated. He never hinted, nor was he asked any questions concerning the possibility, that *Starfish* might have been the cause of this phenomenal rise in radiation.

Dr. Walter Brown, head of the Semi-conductor Physics Research Department at AT&T's Bell Laboratories, defended the joint Government *Starfish* report, saying in February: "The report was justified in painting the blackest possible picture—in being conservative—otherwise it would have whitewashed the whole incident."

NASA officials were still so concerned about the continuing controversy that they issued a special news release in early

February, 1963, stating that there was *no* existing radiation danger to manned space flight as a result of the July *Starfish* test. This was done to allay any public fears over Major Gordon Cooper's safety in his forthcoming 24-hour *Mercury* flight in April.

Dr. Jerome Wiesner, as the President's special assistant for science, was then publicly asked whether America had the moral right to conduct nuclear blasts in space that might affect the welfare of other nations. His answer, given on a coast-to-coast TV program, "The Great Challenge," on February 10, 1963, reflected the administration's continuing posture of after-the-fact moral indignation—despite its before-the-fact ignoring of criticism from scientists, both at home and abroad, who objected to the *Starfish* test in the first place. Wiesner publicly justified the U.S. decision to go ahead with the test "after long consideration" on the ground that the "development of nuclear weapons was related to national security, so steps were taken that we hoped would not be destructive. The government studies convinced us that the results would *not be serious.* Subsequent events *proved they were not.*" [Author's italics.]

His comment appeared to contradict the PSAC report on the results of the test. Wiesner's statement also appeared to be double talk, a Government whitewash of the controversial results of the *Starfish* test, since he believed that "we can't give the decision to an international body—like the U.N.—until we have an international Government. Therefore we can't—at present—give any other nation the right to veto."

But what Wiesner did not say on TV was that even then the administration had information—from a secretly launched satellite—that *Starfish* had indeed been "destructive." He was undoubtedly privy to the real truth of the situation. Less than a month later, in a report issued by the Air Force's Cambridge Research Center Laboratory, an announcement was made of the bare details of five scientific reports that were to be given at an American Geophysical Union meeting in Washington April 17 to 23, 1963. These damning hush-hush reports took the security wraps off *Starad,* a secret satellite that had been hastily assembled in the fall of 1962 after Air Force officers had convinced administration officials that they could get a scientific payload into orbit quickly as a backup for the *Explorer 15* satellite NASA had sent up to check on *Starfish's* havoc.

The experiments in the *Starad* satellite package were secretly rocketed into space from Vandenberg Air Force Base in California on October 26, 1962. The *Starad* (for *Starfish* radiation) was the *only* satellite to furnish comprehensive information on the total increase in the radiation level from the July 9th blast and the two Soviet high-altitude nuclear explosions fired on October 28 and November 1, 1962. It transmitted back much valuable scientific information on the broadened hem of the Van Allen belts until January 18, 1963, when its batteries wore out. It was indeed fortunate that we had *Starad* as a backup vehicle, since *Explorer 15,* which was placed successfully in orbit on October 27th, failed to despin properly, thus making only a limited number of wide-angle radiation observations.

The specific results of the *Starad* satellite's findings were kept secret on the order of Wiesner and Dr. Joseph Charyk, undersecretary of the Air Force, since the existence of this secret "scientific" satellite and its classified findings proved quite embarrassing to the administration. Many politicians in Washington maintained that the image of the U.S. had suffered abroad because the *Starfish* explosion had upset the balance of nature. Wiesner and the PSAC scientists, embarrassed at the results of the shot which went against their predictions, had retreated behind the protection of their delayed release of unfavorable information by recommending that *Starad's* findings be kept secret for a prolonged period. The reports were therefore not given at the Geophysical Union Conference when it convened.

This tactic was accomplished by withholding information about the upsetting disturbance of the natural Van Allen radiation belts until it was published in scientific papers, months after the findings originally became known. This stalling maneuver staved off the unfavorable response that would doubtlessly have resulted had the information been imparted in a press release or at a news conference. Some administration officials applied pressure on Dr. Wiesner and the science advisers to keep the evidence secret as long as possible by waiting until another later scientific conference came along to release the data. In this way, the information would unsensationally filter down to the public.

Meanwhile, Dr. Van Allen finally admitted on March 15, 1963, that the radiation belts which he discovered *had* been disturbed so much by the *Starfish* and other 1962 H-bomb tests that some future space experiments and tests would have to wait *ten* years for the rings to settle back into their normal pattern. Van Allen explained his change of mind about the duration of the artificial belts in these words: "It's the difference between intuitive expectations and actual observations." His latest observations showed that a hem had indeed been added to the skirt of the hopped-up lower Van Allen belts.

On April 18th, Van Allen made another attempt to rationalize his feelings about the results of the *Starfish* blast. He told a group of fellow scientists that the "scientific benefits" of the new artificial belts would "far outweigh the negative effects." Therefore, he said, we shouldn't "worry about upsetting the balance of nature."

And so Van Allen's original "intuitive expectations," which led to his scientific reassurances back in early 1962 that there was no danger of any great disturbances occurring within the radiation belts, had come full circle. The latest scientific findings based on *Starad* proved that his first predictions had been quite fallible.

Gerard Piel, publisher of the *Scientific American,* used the *Starfish* case as a prime example of breakdowns in the channels of communication between the Executive Department and the public on these complex scientific policy matters. He was con-

cerned with the paucity of open discussion and the secrecy
surrounding the merits of the issue before the decision was
made to light up the sky on July 9th.

The *Starfish* controversy has led to several other philosophical
questions about the future of similar H-bomb explosions in
space conducted by either the U.S., the U.S.S.R., or some other
nation. If enough high-altitude nuclear explosions were staged
at frequent, regular intervals in order to maintain a sufficiently
high level of radiation both in the "clear slot" area and below
the inner Van Allen belt, then any hostile satellites could be
disabled. (Of course unprotected friendly satellites would also
be knocked out by the neutralization caused by such a long-
term radiation dosage in space.) This cumulative electronic
poisoning of a satellite's solar cells and other vital parts would
threaten any enemy military satellites orbiting the earth.

*Starfish* has also taught our Government, NASA, the Pentagon, the Soviets and the United Nations, that peaceful, scientific satellites like *Telstar* and *Explorer* can be used successfully to detect nuclear explosions in space. In this respect they
serve a double function—their primary one to increase man's
knowledge of space, and secondarily, as an orbital "black box
inspector," able to warn the rest of the world if some nation
sets off a nuclear blast within the geomagnetic trap surrounding
our earth.

The *Starfish* controversy refused to stay buried. Every time
someone high up in Government circles tried to suppress further open discussion of the test results, the dispute would erupt
on a new front. Usually, the critics were individual scientists
(who were not members of PSAC). Their forums were professional conferences, where they had responsive audiences. Press
conferences at these gatherings kept the public aware—and
kept the fire stoked under the dark *Starfish* cloud that wouldn't
blow away—no matter who tried to make it go away.

Unknowingly, American—and some British—scientists were
taking part *openly* for the first time in a great public debate, not just as advisers, but as responsible, concerned

citizens who had subconsciously and consciously undertaken a campaign to warn the uneducated public about the possible aftereffects of such experiments in the future. No matter who was right or wrong in the controversy, the scientists were expressing their *moral* feelings for the welfare of their fellow men. In this respect, they had moved another step closer to the center of the political stage and farther away from the quiet cloister of their laboratories.

Unfortunately, there is no international agency to which any nation—even if it wished—can go for a judgment on a space project like the controversial *Starfish* experiment. No organization, including the neophyte U.N. Committee on the Peaceful Uses of Outer Space, has been set up and approved as a *regulatory* agency with proper technical apparatus to handle such requests. Furthermore, such decisions are basically not *scientific* but *political* decisions. Therefore, the International Council of Scientific Unions, which has the competency to muster scientific judgments on such delicate issues, will probably not be given authority to render decisions on similar controversial and politically sensitive scientific matters in the future.

What is urgently needed is a new organization, preferably within the United Nations, which will have the proper regulatory authority on all questionable future space experiments. It could be patterned after the successful International Telecommunications Union, the respected authority for regulating the use of world-wide radio frequencies. Such an agency, under the U.N., would set a sound precedent for further expansion of *operations* in the cosmos being superimposed on the U.N.'s present predominantly *advisory* role.

The hassles over the *Starfish* that wouldn't die marked another milestone in the scientists' move to a more active participation in the affairs of the nation and the world. The manmade *Starfish* space bomb, born on July 9, 1962, in the rarefied fringes of space high over the Pacific, will live in the minds of men—as long as this planet survives.

# PART II

## Some Controversial Political Questions
## about Science

In the 20 years since the dramatic event in Chicago [when nuclear fission was first achieved], our progress in the use of science has been great, but our progress in ordering our relations small. We must work even harder . . . to release the creative energies of man so that the scientific revolution symbolized by the atom can be devoted fully to man's welfare.

> —*President John F. Kennedy*
> Message on the 20th anniversary
> of world's first controlled
> sustained nuclear chain reaction,
> December 2, 1962

# Chapter 12

# Do We Need a National Science Policy?

The lack of a well-charted national science policy was glaringly apparent in the spring of 1963 as Vice-President Johnson called on scientists to support his fierce attack on Congress for its questioning of the administration's Gargantuan outer space budget. The Commerce Department took an opposite tack, charging that too many scientific minds were being appropriated for military and space probe programs at the expense of a lagging civilian economy. (The Commerce Department weighted its charge with payroll-sheet proof that two thirds of our scientists have been absorbed into the Pentagon, AEC, and NASA.)

This imbalance exists because it is easier to persuade Congress to vote funds for military and related purposes than for civilian development or economic growth. "We have," the President said in his 1963 Economic Report to Congress, "paid a price [for our defense and space efforts] by sharply limiting the scarce scientific and engineering resources available to the civilian sectors of the American economy." Yet the President has gone along with Congress in perpetuating this imbalance against the advice of such experts as William McChesney Martin of the Federal Reserve Board and others who have argued that the development of new industries is the key to economic growth. Economists point to the decline in the rate of economic growth—from 3.7 per cent in the gross national product during the 1947–54 period to 3.0 per cent in the 1954–60 period—to back up their assertion that the giant sums spent on military and space work have not helped the civilian economy.

"The President has an obligation to choose between the com-

141

peting demands of the Cold War and the economic war," asserts Dr. Herbert Holloman, Assistant Secretary of Commerce for Science and Technology, "and there is a growing feeling that he is not choosing on what is best for the country's future but on what he is most likely to get through a military-minded Congress."

In recent testimony before the House Committee on Government Operations, Dr. Wiesner pointed out the tremendous extent to which the U.S. is devoting its treasures to technological advance. "This fiscal year the President proposes to put about $12.3 billion into research and development—more in one year than the Federal government spent in research and development from the American Revolution through World War II. This $12.3 billion is in effect well over one third of that portion of the budget which is susceptible to control; for a great part of the budget is inevitably committed to fixed requirements such as debt retirement. In addition, Government spends twice as much for research and development as all of industry, universities, and private foundations combined. This budget is not only large but it has been growing at an unprecedented rate—for what in 1950 amounted to $1.2 billion has grown in the intervening years by a factor of 10."

Wiesner's exposition dramatized the need for a clarified national science policy in this era of unprecedented technological change. For despite all these recent moves to strengthen science's governmental role, we still have only a hit-and-miss national science policy. Blame for this failure is due to a combined lack of funds, staff, vision, Congressional support, and also to the opposition of intra-Government agencies unwilling to cede vested interests in their own parochial scientific endeavors.

The National Science Foundation has been limited by an Executive Order to a concern with only "basic scientific research." On many occasions, NSF Director Dr. Alan Waterman has said that his Foundation "is not expected to have responsibility for the applied research and development program of other agencies."

Carl F. Stover precisely summed up the situation in his 1962 pamphlet, *The Government of Science:* "Locating scientific programs in departments and agencies directed to purposes outside of science guarantees that the integrity of science will not receive proper attention. . . . The N.S.F., certainly no match for the D.O.D., is not strong enough to prevent this rape, and weakness of most science units within departments and agencies makes them helpless to protect their own virtue."

At present, the officials making science policy commitments in the various Government agencies are often far removed from those subordinates responsible for fulfilling the commitments. Furthermore, many scientists must depend on decisions made by officials with no scientific competence. If science is to take its rightful place within our governmental framework, these abuses will first have to be overcome.

By 1962, the explosive growth of the Government's involvement in science and technology saw *eleven* Federal departments and agencies supporting major research and development programs.

There are other problems. The NSF has the principal responsibility for conducting research in weather modification, yet at least six other Federal departments are also involved. NASA was told that it couldn't have a Human Factors Branch because similar research was already under way in the Air Force, Navy, and the National Institutes of Health. The Federal Council on Science and Technology, despite valiant efforts, has sadly discovered that coordination of the various science agencies in the Government is virtually impossible. The President's Science Advisory Committee is also hampered, since its temporary "fire brigade" nature cannot adequately substitute for planned permanent administrative policy.

Although some duplication of effort stimulates wholesome competition within the Government, it can be detrimental to the public interest because of an undue burden on the taxpayer. Without a clear, articulate science policy, the path to undesirable science practices, which result only in corrupt science and Government, remains wide open. Policy then usually ends up being determined by the most highly powered publicity program, and expediency takes precedence over reason. Whoever generates the maximum crisis receives the most money.

In the U.S.S.R., the question of *who* makes science policy poses a different, but similar, set of problems. Yevgeniy K. Federov of the Soviet Academy of Sciences recently lamented the scarcity of public exposition by Soviet scientists on the political implications of new scientific developments. He pointed out to his Russian colleagues at their 1959 annual meeting that such participation and contributions by Soviet scientists would not be difficult because they do not have to maneuver between their government's position and scientific objectivity. Presenting to the Russian people the political-social implications of scientific advances is an honor for the Soviet scientist, Federov indicated. In the U.S., by contrast, such free discussion has often prompted Government reprisal.

The Soviet Academy of Sciences' report for 1959 carried the theme of coordination of basic science, applied science, and national policy to such an extreme that only those science programs that furthered the aims of the Communist Party were promoted. Alexander V. Topchiyev, the late vice-president of the Academy, said: "The party teaches us that, when tasks have been determined, it is necessary first of all to organize our forces in such a way as to solve the tasks placed before us with a minimum expenditure of resources and with maximum effectiveness." He then outlined a priority list of 30 most important problems to be studied in the U.S.S.R. While most of these (i.e., the creation of new semiconductor materials, auxiliary substances for the conversion of petroleum, new anticancer antibiotics, etc.) could be directed toward peacetime uses, they could be applied to military ends as well.

Although—unlike the Russians—we have no clearly defined long-range science policy, many thoughtful citizens have been saying it's about time we got one. The basic question of just who would make such a policy—the President? Congress? Scientists in concert?—must first be answered if national scientific goals are to be defined.

If once we agreed on a broad science policy, the question would then be: "Who is going to have the power to set priorities within the framework of the objectives in the national interest?" It is time that we faced up to these questions in order to seek solutions to the larger problem of how to put science to better public use.

Without a national science policy, Congress and the President have no reasonable basis for making decisions about governmental action on the new technological frontiers. We will continue to grope in the dark until definite priorities for scientific programs can be worked out—with the recognition that military considerations must not *always* override important economic, political, educational, and social needs.

Diffusion of responsibility on Capitol Hill has further complicated the problem of establishing national scientific goals. The presidential immunity surrounding PSAC and the Federal Council on Science and Technology, preventing their members from being called before Congressional committees, constitutes a major roadblock to establishment of a sound science policy. The scientific spokesmen from the Pentagon and NASA who have been allowed to appear before the various Congressional committees unfortunately have spoken mainly for the parochial interests of their own organizations.

Tristram Coffin, longtime journalistic observer of the Washington scene, feels that Congress—and particularly the House— maintains a smug "know-nothing" mood on science. The House Space Committee hearings in 1962 with Glenn and the other six astronauts was a "lesson in political buffoonery," Coffin said. He blamed the farce on the Congressmen's "absurd questions." Most Congressmen are from small-town or rural areas and are not interested in science. The few who have shown interest are mostly from the cities.

With over 15 committees on Capitol Hill having a share in legislative action pertaining to science in Government, many scientists and Government officials have suffered fits and frustrations in their attempts to obtain approval for vital projects. It is not surprising, therefore, that so many scientists are concerned about the need for reorganizing the legislative and executive channels through which scientific information flows.

Why should the question of a national science policy come up at this time? After all, we have gotten along for 176 years and become the foremost industrial and technological nation in the world *without* a comprehensive national science policy. Some recent statistics should, in the meantime, supply the answer to the question as to why a national science policy has become essential, in the opinion of many thoughtful citizens— scientists and nonscientists.

As Federal funds for basic research increased from 45 per cent of the total national expenditure in 1953 to 60 per cent in 1961, there was a corresponding decline in the contributions from industries, nonprofit institutions, and other private sources.

This shift toward more reliance on the Federal government for scientific aid has brought about a relative increase in Washington's guidance and control of technology. No longer can American science remain independent of Government action. The 1963 figures for research and development are even more startling. Of the $17 billion (3 per cent of the gross national product) planned for research and development during this year, the Government alone will spend over $12.4 billion. Thus the Federal interest in science has increased to 65 per cent of the national total—up 5 per cent over 1961. This means that either directly or indirectly Washington now employs over 75 per cent of the nation's scientists.

Based on the current research and development growth expenditures, Dr. Alvin Weinberg, head of the AEC's Oak Ridge National Laboratory, has estimated that we will be spending *all* of our money on science and technology by the year 2025. "If Big Science is not to ruin us financially," he concludes, "evidently, something will have to be done." He suggests that scientists start getting used to the idea of settling for an over-all science budget that will never be higher than 1 per cent of the gross national product. Weinberg has made a strong plea for an extensive national debate on the choices we must make as to where in the sciences we should spend our billions of research dollars. "If we don't use a larger slice of this money for civilian and commercial needs we will face the danger of being overtaken by the Japanese, West Germans, and others in our own backyard," he said.

"In making our choices," he warns "we should remember the experiences of other civilizations. Those cultures which have devoted too much of their talents to monuments which had nothing to do with the real issues of human well-being have usually fallen on bad days. . . . So it is for us to learn well these lessons of history: we must not allow ourselves, by shortsighted seeking after fragile monuments of Big Science, to be diverted from our real purpose, which is the enriching and broadening of human life."

Weinberg drew an analogy between Big Science of today, the cathedrals of the Middle Ages, and the pyramids of the ancient Egyptians. Whereas today we build our monuments in the name of scientific truth and to add to our country's prestige, he noted, the theologians of the Middle Ages built their edifices to religious truth and to add to their cities' prestige. "We build to placate what ex-President Eisenhower suggested could become a dominant scientific caste," said Weinberg. "They [the Egyptians] built to please the priests of Isis and Osiris."

Weinberg firmly believes that the President's Science Advisory Committee can establish an over-all science budget and make the hard choices . . . weighing space against biology, atomic energy against oceanography.

Unfortunately Dr. Wiesner, PSAC chairman, has one serious misconception about the present allocation of Federal funds to the sciences. Recently he said he didn't think the behavioral sciences were being hurt at the expense of the natural sciences, since, he believes, they are not in competition with each other for funds. Unhappily, Dr. Wiesner's impression is inaccurate;

the two groups are fiercely competitive. The natural sciences have flourished at the expense of the behavioral sciences, mainly because the social scientists have been less vocal and less able to convince Congress of the importance of their disciplines than spokesmen from the more glamorous natural science fields.

Kenneth Boulding, director of the Center of Conflict Resolution at the University of Michigan and a leading economist, has noted that we are putting our major intellectual and scientific effort and money into defense problems that have no answer, and little if any effort into the solution to real problems. He feels that the people must be awakened to the true nature of the current intellectual crisis if we are to survive.

Weinberg's feeling that PSAC could establish both broad science policy and define priorities is not shared by all of his fellow scientists, many of whom believe Congress should have an important role in the molding of national science policy. Before Congress can play a more active role in shaping the direction of science in the critical years ahead, however, there will have to be drastic reform within Congress itself.

It is generally conceded that present Congressional machinery for handling science (with the exceptions of the Joint Congressional Committee on Atomic Energy and the House and Senate Space Committees) is woefully out of date. The lack of understanding shown by so many politicians of new advances in science has often become a millstone around the neck of progress. There are too few men of the caliber of Senator Clinton Anderson and Representative Melvin Price of the Joint Congressional Committee on Atomic Energy, who possess the basic scientific know-how to enable them to discuss rationally new complex technical programs. Educating members of Congress in the basics of science is essential, but the majority of our Federal lawmakers are unrelentingly hostile to any such "new-fangled book learning."

Besides this problem of getting more knowledgeable, science-minded Congressmen, there is the problem of finding the best avenue for scientists to use in advising Congress. The House

Committee of Science and Astronautics has been the *only* Congressional group that has devoted any time at all to *general* science policy beyond the atom and space fields. Unfortunately, the time has been minuscule, since the great bulk of the Committee's effort is aimed at the more glamorous and pressing space problems. Some observers feel that a new special Joint Committee on Science and Technology or a separate such committee in each house is needed.

To overcome the criticism and fill the science policy vacuum on Capitol Hill, the House Committee on Science and Astronautics announced plans in January, 1962, to undertake "a periodic over-all look at the state of American science." The object would be to keep track of just *where* the United States stands in general science, in each of the major disciplines, and in the educational needs and demands relative to scientists and technicians. The committee members felt they would then be in a better position to advise Congress concerning the problems, needs, demands, ramifications, and solutions to scientific problems.

One year after this announcement was made, this committee had been unable to follow through on its original aim. (When the same House committee tried to hold a one-day science symposium in Washington shortly after the launching of *Sputnik*, the meeting fizzled from poor planning, lack of purpose, and failure to come up with any sound recommendations for an adequate follow-up program. The Congressional Science symposium has never been reassembled.)

It is fairly obvious at present that *no* one group or branch of our Government has been responsible for setting the nation's science policy. In a pluralistic democratic society, this is a healthy sign. However, it also makes for confusion.

Despite the fact that it is not properly organized to handle the Government's burgeoning science activities, Congress does wield immense power over policy and priorities through its control of the purse strings. On this question of priorities for Government science contracts, Democratic Senator Warren Magnuson of Washington, a member of the Senate Space Committee, told a national television audience in February, 1963: "If I had my way, I would put more money into oceanography than space. But I have to take their advice, and so we go *up* instead of *down.*" He admitted that one of the problems that make it difficult for Congress to properly determine priorities is that 19 conflicting Government agencies are interested in some part of the ocean, while a dozen have interests in the space field.

Gerard Piel, publisher of the *Scientific American,* speaking on the same program, said: "The advance of science has confronted society with a new moral choice; either putting our emphasis on space, or in helping the two thirds of the world that are undernourished."

Dr. Wiesner chimed in with his choice. "I feel that the great challenge of our decade is in the underdeveloped areas—to wipe out poverty and disease." Then he added this footnote: "But, in the end, our choice will be made by Congress!"

Even though most old Washington hands concede that Congress does make the choice in the end, the Executive doesn't always spend money for the science projects that Congress approves. Several times in recent years, the Pentagon and the White House have defied the whim of Democratic Representative Carl Vinson of Georgia, chairman of the powerful House Armed Services Committee, to allocate a half billion dollars for building more prototype RS-70 supersonic bombers. This mammoth Air Force project has been labeled "obsolete" and a "waste of the taxpayers' money" by Secretary of Defense McNamara. With the blessing of the President, he has refused to go along with Capitol Hill prodding on this matter.

The controversy over policy making has become a titanic struggle, pitting Congress against the White House. In the exploding space field the question of who sets the national policy is even more perplexing and complex.

The young American space fraternity has failed to find policy spokesmen of a stature comparable to that of the eminent leaders of the nuclear scientists. No space scientist or engineer on the scene today can compare with a Teller, a Rickover, or a Szilard. America has no space scientist-philosopher like the British Arthur Clarke, who theorizes about the future of the cosmos in words the public understands.

Dr. Bernard Feld, an M.I.T. nuclear physicist, who stood with Fermi underneath the bleachers of Chicago's Stagg Field as the atomic age was born one bleak winter morning in December, 1942, believes: "What the new space scientists need is the vision of the abyss or the sense of the devil which some of the older atomic scientists seem to have acquired. If the new space scientists can get this, then they will not need any help. The problem of formulating meaningful national space policy requires as much recognition of the necessity for this formulation as the ability to do something about it. What seems to be lacking is the recognition."

The failure of NASA to lure the cream of American scientists away from industry and the universities is one clue to the failure of the scientific community to speak out in clearer terms about the need for sharing in the responsibility to help formulate a national space policy. Too many scientists do not like working as a "number" on an applied engineering program. They are happier in the laboratory and do not see that the national interest may demand the exploring of space for other than scientific purposes.

Recently, other prominent scientific voices have been heard questioning our national space efforts. Barbs have been thrown particularly at the manned space program by such scientific notables as Vannevar Bush, Lee DuBridge, and Detlev Bronk, head of the Rockefeller Foundation. Dr. Warren Weaver, former president of the American Association for the Advancement of Science, summed up the thinking of this group by saying: "I believe that most scientists consider the proposed [space] expenditures quite unjustified on the grounds of scientific considerations; and also consider the frantic pace of the program to be wasteful." This view is supported by Dr. Killian, who expressed serious doubts about our manned space program less than a year after leaving his post in Washington as the President's science adviser.

In an address delivered at the M.I.T. Club of New York on December 13, 1963, Killian pointed out that since World War II nations have relied increasingly on science and technology as instruments of propaganda and power politics. This trend, Killian reminded his audience, has been most vividly illustrated by the Soviets with their "great and successful efforts—and careful political timing—in space exploration." He continued: ". . . In space exploration, as in all other fields that we choose to go into, we must never be content to be *second* best, but I do not believe that this requires us to engage in a *prestige* race with the Soviets." He then said we should pursue our own objectives in space exploration and should not let the Soviets choose them for us. He feels that our space program should be "in balance" with our other scientific endeavors. Killian fears that we might weaken our technology and actually *lower* our prestige by competing in purely prestige motivated space projects.

Realizing that our man-in-space program is our principal runner in the space race with the Soviets, Killian took his stand with the conservative scientists who are all for calling a halt to our manned cosmic efforts since "many thoughtful citizens are convinced that the really exciting discoveries in space can be realized better by instruments than by man."

In his address to the M.I.T. alumni, Killian urged his listeners to work to "contain" our man-in-space systems and big rocket booster programs before we find ourselves committed to a multibillion-dollar program. No decision to send men to the moon should be made without letting the public in on the startling costs involved, Killian declared. "We should not permit ourselves to slide unwittingly past a point of no return or to make the commitment without comparing its desirability with alternative expenditures," he said.

Although emphasizing that he did not categorically oppose our man-in-space program, Dr. Killian pleaded with his audience to take another look and see if our defense and educational efforts weren't suffering because of our headlong plunge into space. The great scientist continued: "They [the public] must face up to the tough decision . . . whether our system of values assigns greater importance to this kind of exploratory activity or to the development of intellectual quality. Will several billion dollars a year additional for enhancing the quality of education not do more for the future of the United States and its position in the world than several billions a year additional for man in space?"

The fallacy of his thinking in this widely quoted speech lay in his oversimplified either-or alternative. For the knowledge gained from exploits in outer space would not necessarily be diametrically opposed to improving the quality of our inner life, and the money spent on space projects could indirectly benefit our educational system by fostering new science curriculums.

Dr. Bronk, former president of the National Academy of Sciences, feels the prestige involved in America's attempt to land a man on the moon is of *secondary* importance. He thinks the vitality of the human adventure itself is the most important aspect of the dramatic undertaking.

Senator Magnuson sees the goal of a man on the moon in a different light. He feels it would be a step forward for *all* of science, and that it does have political significance. The Senator admitted that this multibillion-dollar project had caused him many a headache. On one hand, some constituents tell him that if we don't get a man on the moon ahead of the Russians they won't vote for him again. On the other side, he receives just as many complaints from those citizens who feel we are spending too much money on space.

After listening to the conflicting views of scientists and non-scientists on the merits of our current space policy efforts, our top space officials have suddenly felt the need to obtain some outside positive scientific advice to help them chart the nation's course in space after 1970. So, four years after the birth of

NASA, they requested the National Academy of Sciences to help them with the task, and, during the summer of 1962, a hundred of America's leading scientists from Government, universities, and industry gathered at the State University of Iowa for an eight-week study of the problem.

On January 5, 1963, the group made their comprehensive recommendations to the space agency. In a 16-chapter survey, *A Review of Space Research,* they said that the nation should give the *highest* priority to the search for life outside of the earth. Such a project, "with its compelling fascination for all nations would do more than anything else in the space race with Russia to enhance our prestige as a peace-loving nation capable of great scientific enterprise," these scientists wrote.

"If life does indeed exist on another planet, and we or the Russians find it," they continued, "that discovery will have an enormous and lasting impact on people of every race and culture the world over." It would also, they said, support the belief that many civilizations comparable to our own may exist on billions of planetary systems throughout the far-flung universe.

Dr. L. C. Van Atta, director of Hughes Research Laboratories, said in the report: "International competition and resulting political commitments have forced upon this complex *Apollo* mission a somewhat unrealistic timetable." But he and the other members felt that we must go ahead with this and other man-in-space programs because it "is the most exciting, challenging, and profound issue, not only of this century, but of the whole naturalistic movement that has characterized the history of Western thought for three hundred years.

"What is at stake," the report goes on, "is an opportunity to gain a new perspective on man's place in nature, a new level of discussion of the meaning and nature of life." The writers warned that the search for life in space has perils that would necessitate the sterilization of our spacecraft to avoid contaminating other worlds with organisms from earth. To best conduct the quest for life in space, they suggested the use of specially trained "scientist-astronauts" perhaps assisted by bands of "automated slave robots" called "telepuppets." Finally, as a group, they recognized that the best of all possible space science instruments was man himself, countering the objections of Dr. Killian and others who had questioned this recent man-on-the-moon emphasis in our space agency's efforts.

In calling for the immediate training of scientists for space flight missions (starting with the *Apollo* project) and the establishment of a sister Institute for Space Sciences next door to the space agency's astronaut training center at Houston, Texas, the scientists were making no mistake as to where they stood within their fraternity on this controversial issue. "Scientists," the report said, "should recognize that *Apollo* is the first phase in a continuing engineering enterprise which will ultimately enable man to move about in space and provide him with the capability for conducting his scientific investigations."

This study represented the *first* comprehensive attempt by a group of distinguished scientists to help chart the course of the nation's space policy. It was the first sign that a cohesive group of experts had been able to agree on what America should be doing with valuable research dollars. Knowingly or not, they had prepared the first scientific-philosophical primer on the space race.

When former President Eisenhower and President Kennedy became involved in an emotionally argumentative public debate over our national space effort in early April, 1963, James Reston of the New York *Times* commented: "The main issue is not one of politics but of priorities. The question is not whether the exploration of space is important, but whether it is more important to put a man on the moon than to get several million men off the dole." Because the violent popular reaction to *Sputnik* deranged both administrations' sense of values and priorities—a derangement aggravated by Congress's zeal to achieve spectacular space victories over the Russians— the balance of our national purposes has been continuously aggravated and distorted.

"Clearing slums and wiping out unemployment raise more controversies on Capitol Hill than shooting John Glenn to the moon," noted Reston. "Accordingly the Administration has in effect said: 'Ask not what is best for the country, but what is easiest to get through Congress.'"

The issue facing the nation is not *whether* we should explore space, but *how* much we should invest in our cosmic budget vis-à-vis the other important areas of our economy. The final decision on the degree of our space exploration will depend on the clarification of our national goals.

It is not enough for one group of space scientists to chart a basic policy in *one* area. If the nuclear, defense, and civil scientists in Government, universities, and industry could prepare similar plans for their respective agencies, and if some central office like Dr. Wiesner's Office of Science and Technology in the White House could put them all together into a codified form—with Congressional approval—then we would have a true natural science policy for the first time in our history.

# Chapter 13

# Should Big Science Have Cabinet Status?

The problem of the proper organization of science in our Government has been with us since 1884, when Congress appointed a commission to consider the establishment of a Department of Science. The National Academy of Sciences was invited to form a committee to assist in the Congressional deliberations. Although no action was taken at the time, the National Academy's committee argued, as many contemporary scientists still are arguing, that "the time is near when the country will demand the institution of a branch of the executive government devoted especially to the direction and control of all the purely scientific work of the government."

In the late nineteenth century, when the Industrial Revolution was just getting under way, and America was still primarily an agricultural nation with transportation geared to the coal-burning iron horse and communication linked to the telegraph, an editorial in *Science,* the official journal of the AAAS, warned:

"The liberal spirit which animates both Congress and the executive departments in their dealings with scientific affairs is very apt to lead them into the support of scientific enterprises without sufficient consideration of the conditions of success and of efficient and economical administration; and a careful consideration of each proposed undertaking by a committee of experts is what is wanted to insure the adoption of the best methods."

If these admonitions made over three-quarters of a century ago had been heeded, the present question of the role science should have in Government would obviously be less controversial.

157

The emergence of scientists to positions of high political influence during the past few years has come about from the role of science in defense, from the rapid increase in public funds appropriated for research, and, in part, from the scientific and technical content of many of the major policy decisions our President has to make.

The increasingly complex scientific aspects of many policy questions prompted President Eisenhower in 1957 to appoint Dr. Killian his special assistant for science and technology. At the same time, Eisenhower broadened the jurisdiction of the President's Science Advisory Committee to encompass all scientific matters it felt should be brought to the President's attention. (Under the Truman Administration, the Committee had been on a stand-by status—available in the event of an emergency.) Eisenhower once again gave the scientific community the direct access to the President which it had enjoyed only once previously, when Vannevar Bush had unlimited entry into the White House during World War II.

More recently, other suggestions have been made to solve our national dilemma over what to do with the organization of science in the Government. In February, 1961, *Fortune* ran an editorial called "An Office of Hairbrained Ideas." The editors of this influential magazine of American business went on record against the establishment of a Department of Science and Technology since "such a vast reorganization of government activities would disrupt more than it would coordinate and we are happy to say that there appears to be little danger of its adoption."

Not content to just debunk such a "grandiose supercoordinating agency," *Fortune* proposed an alternative solution: the establishment of an "Office of Hairbrained Ideas." They admitted that the Government could be counted on to give a "more dignified name" to their "OHI," which would give the President an independent, freewheeling agency, "with money to initiate research in the critical area that lies between basic science and presently developing technology."

The *Fortune* editors felt that their scheme would fill the vacuum which first appeared in 1939, when, for two years, the A-bomb idea went begging in every Government agency—and then only caught on because of a "personal fluke" through the correspondence between Einstein and FDR. The vacuum appeared alarmingly again in the late forties when our large rocket development couldn't get off the ground because the bickering military agencies were extremely skeptical of push-button warfare and because they were convinced that accurate rocket guidance systems were many years away.

*Fortune* desired a resurrection of an organization like the OSRD of World War II, which the magazine termed a "kind of guerilla band of technicians ranging across the whole field of technological possibilities useful in war." Although this agency was swiftly disbanded in 1945 out of fear that the OSRD would compete with private industry in peacetime, now was the time, said *Fortune,* to revive the concept.

The Office of Hairbrained Ideas would be able to "encourage scientists to reach out imaginatively towards advances in those technical areas most significant to government policy." The business magazine warned that the OHI should not be an overlord like that "grandiose superagency—the Soviet Academy of Sciences. This would be incompatible with the American spirit and patently unworkable in the diversity and freedom of American science." Nor should it supplant the present Government military and space agencies, said *Fortune*'s editors, who had a gimmick in their proposal. As soon as a hairbrained R&D project reached the production stage, it should be shifted to Government departments or private industry, "leaving the new agency free of excess administrative baggage." This plea for Government underwriting of the expensive costs of all future R&D was sugar-coated by the argument that advanced research "has to be set up as an entirely separate maverick organization of an entirely different intellectual cast than ordinary research. It must attract the unorthodox, the radical, the creative."

In conclusion, the *Fortune* editors warned their readers that their OHI would not be "infallible" but it is "about the only major hope of staying ahead in a world of fast technological change."

The *Fortune* idea didn't catch on with either the scientists or Washington. Instead of an OHI to overcome inertia on a national scale, the President proposed, and Congress approved, the establishment, under Dr. Wiesner, of the far different Office of Science and Technology, with no contracting powers. And this is where the Government and science stand today.

Wiesner wants his staff to remain compact, since he disclaims any dreams of bigness. He hopes that his office will always serve in a consultant capacity, rather than an executive role, which he feels would lead only to bureaucratic encrustation. "We deal in ideas and problems, not in power plays," he says.

In practice, the special assistant has served as chairman of the President's Science Advisory Committee, though at the choice of the Committee itself, since it was felt that this body should be able to act independently of the political commitments attending a member of the President's staff. The members of PSAC thus serve as a board of consultants to the President and his special assistant and represent a wide range of scientific competence. Usually there are ten or so panels, all operating concurrently, studying particular problems. Many of these studies are undertaken because the special assistant has been able to identify policy-making areas, not recognized by his nonscientific administrative colleagues, where science and technology may have an important bearing.

Dr. Harold C. Urey, the Nobel Prize-winning chemist who discovered heavy water, doubts that the U.S. government needs a separate Department of Science, unless it is modeled after PSAC. He feels that it would be dangerous to have all the various scientific activities of the Government segregated into one single department. "All these other departments should have their own scientific groups working for them. I do not believe that science is a natural division of political activity," he concluded.

Vannevar Bush also feels that there is no need for such a department. He agrees with Dr. Lee DuBridge, president of Cal Tech, who recently said of PSAC that "this committee has quietly and effectively rendered enormous service in bringing to the President, the Cabinet, and the National Security Council, the best science advice in the country on problems of national defense, international relations, public health, education, and encouragement of research. If this organization is kept strong, there will be no need for a Secretary of Science." Justification for this view can be found in the reduction of the possibility of error through the multiplication of judgments. The argument for *many* science advisers, instead of *one,* holds great weight in a democracy.

Dr. James Warwick, who has clashed with PSAC on numerous occasions, has some reservations about the function of advisers. "By doing things in committee form," he said recently, "you come up with conservative decisions, not necessarily the right ones. . . . After the decision has been made . . . the governmental scientific structure needs to *inform* the scientific community on the background of what has to be done, to the extent it can be done outside of bona fide military security considerations."

He also feels that, because space has and will continue to have such vital political and scientific roles in the nation's welfare, PSAC should have adequate representation from the fields of astronomy and geophysics. "Instead," said the Colorado astronomer, "the composition of the committee tends to be dominated by Nobelists, . . . [who] are by the legal prescriptions of Nobel, invariably physicists." Warwick pointed out that the "only representative of the astronomical point of view [on the present PSAC] in any sense of the word is Edward Purcell. Yet his interests are far narrower than geophysics and astrophysics."

But PSAC isn't the only group serving the President on thorny technical problems. For the first time in our history the Government has set up a unit called the Panel on Civilian Technology. This little-known group was established strictly for the purpose of encouraging technological innovation on the premise that new technology stimulates economic growth as much or more than new plants and equipment investment. The 18-man panel, composed of academicians, scientists, industrialists, and bureaucrats, is especially concerned with the *four* industries suffering most from technological lag: textiles, housing, coal, and transportation. It reports to Science Adviser Wiesner, Economic Adviser Walter Heller, and Secretary of Commerce Luther Hodges. It has quickly become a center of controversy because its first report on urban transportation argued against subsidy supports for rail transit and instead favored express buses on exclusive rights of way.

Wiesner hopes that eventually each cabinet secretary and Federal agency administrator will appoint an assistant secretary who could act as an adviser on science and technology. Such advisers might not be able to do away with the narrow mission-bias parochialism of their respective departments, but they could help to spread scientific intelligence and perspective throughout the Government. Actually the assistant secretaries would be wearing several hats—including that of scientific education and public relations.

So far, three members of the Kennedy cabinet—Stewart L. Udall in the Interior Department, Rusk in State, and Hodges in Commerce—have accepted and acted on the idea, and a fourth, Orville Freeman, in Agriculture, is also interested. Udall is particularly delighted with his first science adviser, Dr. Roger Revelle (appointed on the advice of Wiesner), who has been of immense help to him. In the summer of 1961, Revelle and Wiesner went to Pakistan on a research mission after an urgent call for help by President Ayub Khan during his state visit to Washington. They probed the problem of the rising underground water level that was drowning Pakistan's crops, and came up with the solution: pump the underground water to the surface and use it for irrigation. They also made recommendations for the modernization of Pakistan's primitive agricultural program to help her catch up with the rest of the world.

On July 9, 1962, Wiesner, while still serving as acting director of the OST, appeared before the House Subcommittee on Appropriations and affirmed that in his opinion the creation of a Department of Science in the Cabinet would *"not* solve the problems that we are trying to solve. I think you can make an argument for a Department of Science that might bring together agencies like the Weather Bureau, the Bureau of Standards, and a number of other activities and give them greater strength.

"However, if there was a Cabinet officer for such a department," Wiesner commented, "he would be a competitor with the Cabinet officers who had other scientific responsibilities; therefore he could not be given the overall assessment responsibility. Consequently there would still be need for a White House mechanism to provide overall assessment, policy guidance and general technical assistance. . . ."

When asked by Democratic Senator John Tower of Texas, a week later, for his opinion of the proposition concerning the establishment of a Department of Science with Cabinet status, Wiesner commented with some ambivalence: "I really am of two minds regarding it. I think that some of its proponents would feel that a science department would provide coordination, that is a coordination and a pulling together of the scientific program of the government and an avoidance of duplication. I do not believe that complete coordination is possible. I would be very much against putting them all in one agency." (Later, he went on record for putting the NSF and NASA together to provide a "single, strong voice for science"— but that was as far as he went.)

Neither was Wiesner sure that any substantial improvement in the management of scientific programs would result by having the head of such a collective department sitting in the Cabinet.

"My own view of the problem," he concluded, "is that we should try to get the very best people into the agencies. . . . That is what we need more than anything else, and if we succeed in finding them, many problems we are now worried about will disappear."

Senator Magnuson expressed a different view when he recently predicted that we are gradually going to have to come to accept the need for a Secretary of Science. "Why, Wiesner is at the sub-Cabinet level now," he said, "and is slowly working himself into the post, over the strenuous objections of many of his fellow scientists."

Besides Magnuson's broad hint, in recent years there have been several other proposals dropped into the Congressional hopper to give America a Department of Science and Technology headed by a Cabinet secretary. Such a post—it is argued—would give the secretary a broad range of Government responsibilities and provide for more effective program coordination. Its proponents also argue that the department would be the focal point of policy deliberations, help to build a more substantial organizational environment in Government that would be conducive to scientific work, and, finally, would provide Big Science with a voice of stature equal to that of other Federal departments—like the Post Office.

Dr. Wallace Brode, when he was science adviser to the State Department and president of the AAAS, recommended that a Secretary of Science be appointed to the Cabinet. Although many bills to set up such a post have been introduced in Congress, none has ever passed either house. The opinions of the scientists themselves are still too divided to make any positive action on the question possible.

Dr. Wallace Sayre of Columbia University has noted that the proposal to give science a voice at the Cabinet table has encountered the "stubborn pluralism of the scientists themselves." The opposition of Government scientists, more willing to endure the existing familiar organizational environment than to risk the unknowns of a new and untested arrangement, has contributed to Sayre's conclusion that "a Department of Science, then, waits upon the unlikely event that the scientists will . . . conclude that they are sufficiently unified to risk their separate interests to the leadership and fortunes of a single government institution."

There are thousands of different views on the matter, but, as yet, no unanimity from within scientific circles as to whether the potential virtues of a Cabinet-level Department of Science would outweigh its vices. It is, however, absurd to believe that if such a step is ever taken by the White House, *all* Government activities related to science will be moved automatically under the wing of the new agency. Dr. James Fisk, president of the Bell Laboratories, said recently: "To imagine that 'science' as a whole could be abstracted from government departments and agencies and set up somehow as a separate department—a Department of Science—is, I believe, unrealistic. It would be somewhat analogous to abstracting 'economics' from these departments and agencies and forming a Department of Economics."

Granted that the uses of scientific ideas pervade every branch and agency of our Government and that some, like the soil and crop research programs of the Department of Agriculture, are integrally tied to the operating responsibilities of that agency, the question is asked: "Can we remove a *part* of the science program from various Government agencies, without destroying the *whole* program of that department?"

The establishment of a Department of Science would necessitate many adjustments and changes in the present Government-science organization chart. Perhaps the advocates of Cabinet status for science could take a cue from NASA and start out with a minimal program, expanding its activities as time and experience so dictated. Such a department would not only have the responsibilities for policy planning and program coordination, but would also have the main function of support of basic science. This would include the administration of major research grants and facilities.

As NASA started out in life by absorbing and building on NACA, so a new Department of Science and Technology could start out by absorbing the NSF, the PSAC, and the FCST as its foundation. By merging these present agencies under one roof, it would strengthen them and add to their effectiveness. At the same time, it could draw cooperatively from the other large Government agencies, like the Department of Defense, NASA, and the AEC with their special scientific resources.

Besides overseeing and supporting *basic* research, the new department should be able to conduct its own *applied* scientific research. It could also absorb under one roof such present Government-science programs as the Weather Bureau (Commerce), the National Bureau of Standards (Commerce), Geological Survey and the Bureau of Mines (Interior), the Office of Saline Water (Interior), the Hydrographic Office (Navy), the Coast and Geodetic Survey (Commerce), the Naval Observatory, the research activities of the Smithsonian Institution, and the Antarctic Office (Navy). There is no rational explanation or virtue to the present organizational location of any of the units cited. The Weather Bureau started out in life under the Department of the Army, then was transferred to Agriculture, and later on to Commerce, where it has no particular tie other than historical. It could fulfill its functions better under a Department of Science. Although the National Bureau of Standards serves industry, it receives only half of its budget from the Commerce Department's appropriations, and the rest elsewhere. So a transfer—to a department where science is a central theme and not a side issue—would appear to be in order.

Although such burgeoning Government agencies as NASA and the AEC are heavily oriented toward scientific research, they are already so large that they might possibly overwhelm the new department. Therefore, they would best remain independent to conduct their own operating programs for the time being. (The author has already proposed in his book, *The Space Race,* published in 1962, that NASA is already big enough to warrant Cabinet status—right now.) Possibly a trade could be made by demoting the Post Office back to its proper place as an independent agency without Cabinet status—or as a subordinate branch of the Commerce Department, where it more rightfully belongs. Then we could boost Science to Cabinet rank and NASA to a sub-Cabinet department eventually under Science. This move would make sense if for no other reason than to correct the current disparity between budgetary status and rank. Whereas the Post Office spends $700 million annually, NASA is currently spending almost $6 billion and will soon be gobbling up an average of *at least* $10 billion a year for the rest of this decade. In time, a new sub-Cabinet department of Oceanography could also be established as part of the Science department. Then this new agency would encompass land, water, and space under one roof.

The expanding AEC could even conceivably be amalgamated with the Interior Department (which could become a sub-Cabinet branch of Science), and which is responsible for operating most of our large publicly owned hydroelectric energy efforts outside of the TVA. The kinship between these two agencies as basic fuel suppliers to the nation's growing needs in electrical and atomic power could bring them together in the future. Liaison offices with NASA and the Pentagon would still have to be kept in any setup.

In placing the responsibility for science and technology in the hands of a single Cabinet officer, a new Department of Science would have many advantages. It would finally provide a focus for the development of a national science policy. It would increase the communication and cooperation between the Executive Branch and Congress because of the availability of the Secretary and his staff for Congressional inquiry.

Incidentally, it is time that PSAC was also promoted to permanent full-time status—with part-time consultants called in as needed. This transfer would eliminate the present PSAC's problem of having to rush through the agenda whenever it meets. The Research Section of the Industrial Union Department of the AFL-CIO has recently made a similar recommendation by suggesting the establishment of a "Permanent Commission on Technological Change" in the Executive Branch to act as a "central clearinghouse in which there will be gathered, analyzed, and evaluated all pertinent information on public and private plans involving technological change."

The Secretary of Science would undoubtedly become a permanent member of the National Security Council, since so many of the Security Council's recent problems have a scientific base. (There is already a working pattern for such a Supra-Science Department within the Pentagon. Dr. Harold Brown, director of research and engineering in the Department of Defense, has budgetary control over the research and development programs of the three services.) The Secretary of Science would also be in a position to apply pressure where necessary in the vast Federal bureaucracy to improve the rate of scientific advance. The possibility of too much concentration of power in the hands of a Secretary of Science would be offset by the integrative benefits of his office.

A new Science Department would also serve America as the first effective counterbalance to the military control of science. Today the Pentagon budget is so large that it tends to dominate science, whereas a Science Department could act as a counterforce to this trend.

A Cabinet post for Science would also probably do more than any other single move to help our budding scientific statesmen to become aware of the national and international problems beyond the parochial problems of their own specialties. It would also help to attract more competent scientists and engineers into Government service at higher salaries.

These arguments carry great weight for the eventual establishment of a Department of Science with a Secretary at the Cabinet level in Washington. The only unanswered question is when this final move to the top rung of the ladder will occur. Probably, it will take place the day after the first Soviet cosmonaut lands on the moon.

# Chapter 14

# Can Scientists Both Advise and Make Policy, Too?

In September, 1959, Senator Kenneth Keating (who more recently has been President Kennedy's chief critic of our Cuban policy) found himself involved in a debate with Dr. Pascual Jordan, professor of theoretical physics at the University of Hamburg. The New York lawmaker felt that in the Western world scientists should be on tap as counselors and advisers to Government; but they should not try to be politicians, since their training does not equip or qualify them for the job.

After praising the scientists for educating the general public and succeeding as informants of mankind, Keating then took them to task for dabbling in politics. "When they nourish a campaign for banning or controlling atomic weapons and for stopping atomic tests," he said, "or rush into a crusade to compel the U.S. Administration to reach some peaceful sort of misunderstanding with the Soviets before it is too late, or campaign for world government as the sanest solution" without enough apparent realization of the difficulties, "they have often contributed not to the enlightenment, but to the confusion of free men everywhere." He ridiculed the way Szilard and other atomic scientists had tried to oppose the further use of nuclear weapons.

Scientists fail as politicians—according to Keating—because they do not "gauge the political, that is, the human factors of the situation" and they "overestimate the influence of reason in human affairs." He also thought that the scientists "tend to consider the elimination of future war as a problem of logic, rather than of passions, power, and truly conflicting human aims and interests." Politics is not as superficial and easy as most scien-

169

tists feel, because there is no sure test, no certainty, and no objective criterion, according to the New York Senator. He further believed that "once a scientist is convinced of an idea, he often becomes incapable of changing his mind even when faced with new facts." For this reason, Keating asked the scientists to exercise self-restraint by making a clear-cut division between science and politics, by confining their political activity to providing information, and by not trying to become policy makers.

On the other side of the argument, Dr. Jordan felt that scientists *should* participate in politics. Western scientists concerned with threats to the democratic way cannot divorce their scientific efforts from political efforts to insure democracy's continued existence, he declared. Since scientists feel that scientific progress depends on an atmosphere of intellectual freedom, they cannot remain aloof from politics, because the democratic way requires participation of *all* segments of the population. If we disqualify one group, Dr. Jordan said, then we can keep others out, too; so the Government would then be run only by political experts, and democracy would cease to exist.

Jordan warned his listeners that we must not expect scientists to become "political miracle men." Given such status, scientists would approach great world problems with the conviction that they had to introduce entirely new methods into politics. Jordan recommended instead that scientists should give greater support to the political institutions of democracy. But he avoided any discussion of *how* scientists were to cooperate and carry out their new civic duties.

Jordan forgot to point out that, since the typical scientist is *more* than just another John Doe, his advisory pronouncements on controversial questions carry a weight *far* greater than those of an ordinary man. Scientists' use of public forum to air personal prejudices without giving sufficient study to the problem has caused many of our political leaders to be wary of their pronouncements. Many observers feel this breach can be mended only if scientists realize that, by acting responsibly, they will earn more respect in political circles.

The Keating-Jordan debate disclosed the gulf between the politicians and the scientists. Jordan and his fellow scientists' preoccupation with "the scientific method," which, they feel, only they are capable of understanding, is the cause of much of the conflict between them and the rest of society. The scientists' attitude was well expressed by a Nobel Prize winner, Dr. Albert Szent-Gyorgi of the Marine Biological Laboratory in Woods Hole, Massachusetts, in an article in the October 20, 1962, issue of the *Saturday Review*. He concluded: "The only way out is to apply to political questions the same humble, honest, objective approach that has characterized the development of science. Yet there is not at present one scientist in Congress. Scientists are consulted, but only on technical questions, not on basic issues of policy. Unfortunately, the electorate will not vote for scientific-minded people until it can think scientifically itself, and in this it has a long way to go."

Tragically, when the scientist does apply his brains to a pressing human problem, he usually comes up with a "scientific" solution—that is, mechanistic, tidy, and oblivious to human passions, prejudices, traditions, fear, greed . . . and political realities.

The recent emergence on the American scene of the technological monster known as "Big Science" is the most obvious result of increased Government doting on science for advice and policy help. "Big Science" is a title coined by Dr. Alvin Weinberg, director of the Oak Ridge National Laboratory, to connote the large science organizations—such as the atomic bomb laboratories and the massive, complex industrial and governmental research facilities—that have sprung up in recent years. It is a label for the *groups* of scientists who are called upon today to do the jobs that *individuals* like Edison and Steinmetz performed alone in the past. Some scientists, among them Weinberg, believe that Big Science is ruining science. He analyzed the problem recently in the authoritative journal, *Science,* with the following astute observation:

"Since Big Science needs great public support it thrives on publicity. The inevitable result is the injection of a journalistic flavor into Big Science which is fundamentally in conflict with the scientific method. Issues of scientific or technical merit tend to get argued in the popular, not the scientific press, or in the Congressional committee room rather than in the technical society lecture hall. . . .

"One sees evidence of the scientists' spending money instead of thought. This is one of the most insidious effects of large-scale support of science. . . . The line between spending money and spending thought is blurring.

"Finally, the huge growth of Big Science has greatly increased the number of scientific administrators. Where large sums of money are being spent there must be many administrators who see to it that the money is spent wisely. Just as it is easier to spend money than to spend thought, so it is easier to tell other scientists *how* and *what* to do than to do it oneself. The big scientific community tends to acquire more and more bosses . . ."

Dean Don Price of Harvard has coined a similar-sounding phrase—the Scientific Establishment—to describe Big Science. He noted recently, "The plain fact is that science has become the major establishment in the American political system; the only set of institutions for which tax funds are appropriated almost on faith." He has elevated this establishment to that of a "new priesthood allied with military power."

These scientific administrators that are multiplying faster than any other type in Washington these days are policy makers in their own right. They are not predominantly advisers, although they are still called upon from time to time to render advice to their nonscientific political superiors. Because their growing policy-making activities were seen as a threat to their departmental chieftains' authority, a warning to the scientists was handed down by a high White House official in late 1962.

Just before he triggered a crisis in the Canadian Parliament by trying to force nuclear weapons on our northern neighbor without first consulting either them or the State Department, McGeorge Bundy, President Kennedy's special assistant for national security matters, told the scientists that they should not do what he himself was to do so shortly thereafter. He pleaded with several thousand scientists on December 27, 1962, to respect their calling. "This means that he [the scientist] should carefully limit the occasions on which he speaks ex cathedra so that he is not placed in danger of losing his reputation," Bundy said.

He went on to point out how dangerous it was for scientists to take unbending positions on such acute problems as the diffusion of atomic know-how among countries such as China, and the chances of accidental explosions touching off a nuclear war. "These are very great problems indeed," said Bundy, former dean of Harvard, "and they have engaged the prayerful attention of our national leaders for years. It is dangerous for the scientist to adopt an either-or attitude on these complex problems." He then lambasted Sir Charles P. Snow for predicting two years earlier that the Chinese would have the atomic bomb within five years. This nonscientist went on record suggesting that the British scientist's flat assertion on this atomic problem was just "not so" because it "touched on the political realm," a sacred territory into which he should not have trespassed.

Yet Bundy saw no contradiction between this advice and his own offhand policy making less than two months later, when he spoke publicly about American "gifts" of nuclear armed missiles to Canada.

Sir Charles Snow had previously pointed out in one of his Godkin Lectures at Harvard the *hazards* of a head of state's getting his scientific advice principally from *one* individual, especially on matters not open for public review and debate. "Both the policy maker and the science adviser have a responsibility to minimize the danger of biased or highly personalized advice on secret matters, especially in areas of science and technology that can be fateful to the security of a nation," the controversial British scientist declared.

The "objective" science expert will inevitably be called upon to make political judgments, along with scientific ones, in advising on confidential matters of state. Robert Gilpin, in his book *American Scientists and Nuclear Weapons Policy* (Princeton, 1962), has divided this confused middle ground of scientific advice in Government into the realm of *science,* or WHAT IS, and the realm of *policy,* or WHAT IS TO BE DONE. Most scientists advising on nuclear weapons have to combine scientific and political judgment. Therefore, there is no longer any "pure" scientific advice. Although the typical scientist tries to remain coldly objective at all times, it is difficult for him to free himself from his nontechnical assumptions and his moral values. "The values of a scientist are an integral part of his research," wrote Gilpin. "These values affect the problems he selects for study, the facts which he believes are relevant and the implications or hypotheses he draws from the facts."

Gilpin concluded that "both scientists and political leaders have acted as if it were possible to make a clear delineation between the political and the technical realms. This simplistic view of the scientist's role as adviser has created expectations which the scientist cannot fulfill. He is expected by political leadership, fellow scientists, and his own conscience to render only objective technical advice. As a consequence . . . scientists have been assigned many apparently 'technical' tasks whose performance has required a political skill far beyond their competence; scientists and political leaders have failed to realize the nature of the nontechnical assumptions underlying the scientists' advice; and scientists have charged one another with intellectual dishonesty when they have disagreed strongly with advice which has been given."

These disagreements have been dramatized in the Air Force's RS-70 and TFX airplane controversies and NASA's *Apollo* man on the moon program.

The one flaw in Gilpin's thesis is his statement that "American scientists, at least in the area of national policy towards nuclear weapons, have become full partners with the politicians, administrators, and military officers in the formulation of policy." He failed to point out *who* picks the scientists called upon to participate in policy making and *when* they are listened to by Government administrators. We need some way of judging their advice earlier in the game, so that we do not have to wait for their memoirs to discover the reasons for their stands.

Dr. Killian, on the other hand, believes that in certain kinds of technical questions scientists will respond with objectivity and integrity. "In these situations," says Killian, "the adviser must state the facts, including their differences, and list the alternative interpretations of which the policy maker must be aware. As science gets more and more involved in controversial policy decisions, both the policy maker and the body politic must understand that scientific method and analysis do not always yield a single, incontrovertible answer. There are, of course, many questions to which the scientist can give positive answers, the correctness of which can be demonstrated, but he sometimes has to resort to 'dusty' answers when the policy maker understandably is 'hot for certainty.' "

Killian feels that checks and balances to insure the best scientific advice can be attained through proper organization. He feels that the direct-access door to the President, which his Science Advisory Committee had at all times, opens the way to a route the committee can use to bring in alternative opinions and independent positions whenever its members disagree with the Special Assistant for Science and Technology. As a board of consultants to the special assistant, the PSAC can also give the President the benefit of varied points of view, and, Killian says, "if he is wise, he can use it to test his judgment and insure against his own prejudices" becoming dominant. "This mechanism has worked well under the last two Presidents, since both the Science Adviser and PSAC realize that their effectiveness rests on their ability to maintain the confidence of both the President and the scientific community."

Dr. James Warwick of the High Altitude Observatory in

Boulder, Colorado, goes beyond Killian. He does not believe that there is "any distinction in a real sense between scientific and political advice. Scientists don't consider that the world of science stops at the skin-level of the two billion human beings on the surface of the globe; and, equally, political officials do not consider that their domain fails to extend to the atmosphere and beyond. The question . . . is not *what* we discuss but *how* we discuss it."

"The problem," he points out, "is that over a vast range of human affairs, we do not, nor are we in the measurable future likely to have, nor perhaps is it even desirable that we ever have, predictability. But, in order for the biological organisms on this planet to survive in this scientific world, decisions must be taken that are essentially nonscientifically based just in order to get on with the affairs of the world."

He feels there is a great danger today that these essentially political decisions will be turned around and justified to the world on a scientific basis. "The dividing line between science and politics seems to be more and more crossed," he says. Warwick admits that a politician might underestimate his own powers of assimilation of the scientific facts about the real world around him. Since the real world is so important to the politician, Warwick hopes that the close relations already established between senior scientists and legislative and executive department leaders will continue to grow. "One could even hope," he adds, "that this kind of arrangement would become normal at the state and local legislative level."

Not all scientists share Warwick's views on the issue of advice *vs.* policy. Many take the more conservative view expressed by Dr. Harold Brown, director of defense research and engineering, who has stressed that, while it is important for scientists and engineers to give technical advice to those responsible for decisions, "technical advice is only one factor in the decision."

"Military advice," he wrote, "is necessary to given information on the importance of new weapons that might come from additional testing, and political advice is necessary on the impact on international affairs of a decision to do nuclear testing. The advice on each of these factors—technical, military and political—must come from experts in the field, and the scientists and engineers have the responsibility for only *one* of them."

Brown conceded, however, that "a scientist or engineer in government, being an informed person, may have opinions on matters beyond his technical sphere of responsibility." He saw no objection to the scientist expressing such opinions on non-technical matters so long as the views are clearly identified as opinions of an informed nonexpert. But these opinions often spill over into the gray area between advice and policy. Dr. Jerome Wiesner, the President's assistant for science and technology, has pointed out that the scientist, seeking *the* solution to a political problem, is usually not satisfied with short-step accommodations, such as those that comprise the bulk of political actions. Wiesner says scientists often impatiently strive to solve our problems with larger measures, despite their high degree of risk.

Another prominent scientist, Dr. Harrison Brown, recently commented on one of the reasons for the impatience shown by so many scientists in Government. "One of the more serious difficulties in the past," he said, "has been that, with few exceptions, department heads have not been research-minded, with the result that research and development have been relegated to the lower regions of the priority list. The advice of top scientists in various departments and agencies has, all too often, gone unheeded. The lack of attention given to scientific-technological problems by political appointees has often resulted in the perpetuation of provincialism in a number of the agencies, as well as in the creation of atmospheres which have seriously impeded proper intellectual and physical growth."

Brown sees some hope of having the National Academy of Sciences-National Research Council play a mediator-catalyst role when scientific-political policy matters reach a temporary stalemate. The NRC is a quasi-governmental organization which, during the last few years, has contributed substantially in a variety of ways to the formulation of Government programs. Being outside the Government, its members can theoretically examine problems in a more detached way than can governmental persons themselves. Brown hopes the Academy-Research Council will become the major source of scientific-technical advice to Congress. In the past, Congressional Committees have often obtained scientific advice in a rather haphazard way, and the persons giving the advice have not always been as competent as one might wish.

The Academy-Research Council structure needs to be "strengthened to the point where government agencies and Congressional committees alike, in need of advice, would turn confidently to the organization for recommendations as to how that advice might best be obtained," Brown says. "Congress is going to be concerned more and more during the years ahead with legislation involving scientific and technical matters. The establishment of a strong Academy-Congressional bond appears to make a great deal of sense, provided the Academy-Research Council strengthens itself to the point where it can handle the increased load in a systematic way."

The most noted exemplar of a country where the national academy of science acts as the official advisory and policy coordinating body to the Government is the U.S.S.R. In the spring of 1961, responsibility for coordinating Russia's total research and development effort was established at the highest level in the Soviet government by the creation of the State Committee for the Coordination of Research and Development, with a deputy chairman of the Council of Ministers as its head. The membership of this central coordinating committee includes the president of the Academy, the minister of higher and secondary specialized education, and representatives of each of the important state committees involved with research and development work. The Academy retains its role of exercising scientific and methodological leadership, but its work is focused primarily on the most important long-run problems of science, and it is not concerned with the myriad Soviet technological institutes.

Scientists are now pre-eminent in the Kremlin hierarchy, with 8 out of 15 members of the Communist Party presidium having a technical background. Over half of the party Secretariat and the Central Committee of the Communist Party are made up of leading Soviet scientists and engineers. In 1962, a new Central Steering Committee of the Council of Ministers of the U.S.S.R. was established to coordinate scientific research work and to strengthen the position of science in the Soviet government. This move was in line with Russia's aim to surpass the U.S. by 1980—not just economically, but in making better use of scientific and technological advances.

We in America have a long way to go if our scientists are ever to achieve a comparable status by holding down an equal percentage of key seats in our Government. But the American people may never wish to achieve such a heavily weighted group of scientist-managers in our pluralistic democratic society.

When Khrushchev sacked the vituperative Valerian Zorin from his post as chief U.N. negotiator during the last week of October, 1962, he picked a top Soviet scientist, Vassily Kuznetsov, as a replacement. First Deputy Foreign Minister Kuznetsov, who speaks flawless English, is by trade an engineer. In 1941, he received the Stalin Prize for inventing a high-quality alloy steel. In diplomatic circles Kuznetsov has made an excellent reputation as a flexible conciliator with a sense of humor—a characteristic that so many diplomats and scientists do not possess.

The typical American scientist-diplomat is not as well prepared as Kuznetsov and his Soviet counterparts. Too many of the Americans are in a hurry to return to their former posts; their more professional Soviet colleagues realize their careers are greatly furthered by their conscientiousness and their success in putting across a point for the U.S.S.R. Soviet scientists are forever coming up with new subjects to advance their

Government's cause in international negotiations, while most Americans restrict themselves to the topics on the agenda. It is not surprising that in such an unequal contest, the American is often bested. What we need is more flexibility in our scientific-diplomatic negotiations—a flexibility such as the British have practiced so well over the years.

The confusion and controversial questions still remain unresolved since the days of the dispute over the development of our H-bomb. What does the scientist do when a President or high Government official decides *not* to take the advice of his science advisers? Does he go to Congress and the people with his case, if he feels that the national interest is in danger? Under our Constitutional system there is no simple answer to this dilemma: Should the adviser put loyalty to his country above loyalty to the man he advises?

If a scientist's advice continues to prove unpopular to higher authorities, the risk of criticism and downfall of the adviser might result. High Government scientists can suffer the same fate as Harold Stassen and Lewis Strauss, should they become involved in a controversy from which there is no way out. Oppenheimer's advice against pushing the development of the H-bomb was essentially the reason for his fall from power. As more of our top scientists assume dual policy and advisory posts in the Government, they will face the need to adjust to the dual role of policy maker and adviser in Government.

On March 21, 1963, the Kennedy Administration picked Gerard F. Tape, a 47-year-old physicist and president of the Associated Industries, Inc., to be the new scientist member of the AEC. The appointment of another scientist to the AEC was in line with a policy decision of the administration to bring more scientific influence into the management of the agency. The White House had already broken with past tradition by bringing in a scientist, Dr. Glenn T. Seaborg, to head the AEC.

Capitol Hill did not greet the new scientific domination for the commission with enthusiasm. There was some grumbling among members of the Joint Atomic Energy Committee that scientists were not necessarily best qualified to run an agency confronted with management and policy problems transcending strictly technical issues. The administration, however, felt that this experiment had proved to be a success and should be continued. White House officials also believed that a good balance had been struck in the commission with the present membership of two scientists, two lawyers, and one businessman.

Tape happened to be well qualified within the scientific community, since he possessed the somewhat rare combination of a broad background in scientific research as well as considerable administrative experience. He had been deputy director of the AEC's Brookhaven National Laboratory on Long Island (New York) from 1951 to 1961. In 1962, he had been made president of the nonprofit corporation known as the Associated Universities, set up after World War II by nine Eastern universities to manage the Brookhaven Laboratory for the AEC. Associated Universities subsequently took over the operation of the National Radio Astronomy Observatory in West Virginia for the National Science Foundation.

Tape replaced on the AEC Dr. Leland J. Haworth, a 58-year-old physicist, who, in turn, subsequently replaced the retiring 71-year-old Dr. Alan Waterman as director of the NSF. Haworth—a Republican—who had served for two years as a controversial member of the AEC, made his mark as a scientist-administrator of the AEC's Brookhaven National Laboratory from 1948 to 1961. In his two short years as an AEC commissioner, Haworth developed—somewhat to the consternation of his colleagues—into a powerful political figure who combined his scientific prestige and political acumen to fashion a sphere of influence that stretched from the White House into the commission staff. At times there were jealous grumblings from other commissioners that his influence was too great and that his perspective was too narrowly oriented toward science.

Haworth took his oath of office as the new head of the NSF on June 28, 1963, at a difficult juncture in the rapidly expanding, evolving agency. For the Foundation had suddenly found itself not only responsible for basic research, but also with broadened responsibilities—including the support of scientific education. Its current budget had swelled to a high of $589 million, which was quite a jump from the meager $4.5 million budget with which the NSF began its life in 1951.

His most pressing problem was to disentangle the mismanagement of the $60 million Project *Mohole*, an ambitious engineering endeavor to drill a hole through the earth's crust to the Mohorovicic Discontinuity, a geological region generally accepted as the dividing zone between the crust and mantle. It was hoped that Haworth would carve out a more aggressive policy-making role for the NSF, which his predecessor had looked upon as being more of an advisory agency.

In Britain, there is a clear distinction between advising and policy making. The British setup avoids placing excessive responsibility on the expert, in the belief that excessive responsibility often paralyzes thought. Herman Finer, professor of political science at the University of Chicago, recently pointed out that American politicians have created an atmosphere hostile to the nonpartisan expert. "American public administration," said Finer, "has refused to make the distinction between career administrators and scientists. In American government, scientists get to high posts in departmental hierarchies as Heads of Bureaus. This affects the scientist's impartiality." This situation does not exist in Britain where there is a protective shield supplied by the British administrative class.

To prevent the life of the scientist in U.S. government service from becoming unbearable, Finer feels that there is a dire need for an "intervening layer" of career servants between the scientists and the politicians, similar to that which exists in Britain, France, and Germany. He recommended that a group of these experts should be recruited from the best minds of the young graduates, who have had a science-oriented liberal education. This group could then take over the jobs of fighting for money in Congress, justifying departmental policy, briefing the political chieftains, and taking up arms in the eternal internal struggle among Government departments. In this way, we could treat our intellectual science advisers with more freedom and respect than we have in the past.

The scientists have come of age politically. While most of them have based their opinions and advice on a combination of scientific-political factors, their political acumen and wisdom are not necessarily more correct than or superior to the acumen and wisdom of nonscientists. Scientists must speak out on the public and private uses of their technological inventions. They have been almost universally silent on these issues. It is not so important that they just speak out or be asked for advice, but that they have *something worth while to say* on controversial subjects. This means an awareness of the true nature of our weapons, as well as a willingness to do something about the problem. They must learn to work with the other professional groups who hold views similar to theirs. But no intellectual grouping of the professions will be able to combat the present industry-military elite until they align themselves with social scientists, labor leaders, teachers, and farmers. Together, they can carry the weight to exert constructive influence in our society and in Congress.

The most crucial area of advice giving by qualified scientists to the Federal government is at the point where Congress is about to vote on appropriations. Philip Abelson, editor of *Science,* testified on this sensitive subject before the Senate Committee on Aeronautical and Space Sciences in mid-1963. "At that point," Abelson said, "the Congress gets advice that is almost unanimously of a self-interest kind. There has not been a mechanism for some kind of devil's advocate.

"The Bureau of the Budget tries to function in such a capacity," he went on to say, "but the people in the Bureau of the Budget are not sufficiently independent, are not sufficiently informed. I think it would be very useful if, in these areas involving great appropriations, a group of first-class scientists could be asked to point out what are the negative aspects of scientific projects that are glossed over by the advocates [of these projects].

"Some of my scientist friends are great enthusiasts. They feel there is no end to the amount of money that can be usefully appropriated for science. So there is no restraint on them and they will advocate, and advocate, enthusiastically and forcefully.

"Somehow or other, the role of the devil's advocate should not only be established but the devil's advocate should be given a little bit of due. He should be available to the legislative branch and both the majority and minority party should have some say in calling upon that kind of talent."

In line with this scientist-editor's suggestion, several Congressmen, led by Republican Representative Abner W. Sibal of Connecticut, have recommended that each House of Congress retain not just one, but at least three scientists on its payroll to aid in decision making on these vital issues affecting our future. Ultimately, Congressmen will have their own scientific advisers to help them assess the differences between advice and policy, and what is right for the nation.

# Chapter 15

# Should Scientists Run for Political Office?

The scientist's rise in politics could become the most important single development in the changing political patterns wrought by the technological impact of the Space Age. Dr. Killian recently urged his colleagues to run for Congress. He noted that many were already in various state legislatures. Killian suggested that a technologically oriented society must have scientists "in the public arena if it is to deal wisely with all the great policy matters arising out of science and technology."

Sidney Hook, chairman of the philosophy department at New York University and a noted social scientist, has serious reservations concerning Killian's call to his scientific brethren to help save the world from calamity. "To a scientist," said Hook, "the arena of history and political affairs is bewildering, because he soon discovers that telling the truth is one of the best ways of deceiving his opponents."

As a prime example of the political innocence of the natural scientific mind, Hook pointed to the belief held by Nobel physicist Dr. I. I. Rabi concerning possible Russian evasion of any political agreement over a nuclear test ban. In an August, 1960, *Atlantic* article, Rabi expressed his feeling that we shouldn't mention our fear of this probable course of cold war events because this would be an admission that we thought the Russians would be cheating on us. (The Soviets did just that— without signing an agreement—when they resumed nuclear testing in the atmosphere two months later.)

In late 1961, Vannevar Bush admonished his fellow scientists to respect "those individuals who are masters of the art of operating in the confused area of the American political scene." He felt that if our scientists are to have their "full influence in the days to come, many of them will indeed need to learn to practice this difficult art" of politics.

A need for re-education and development of political sophistication has plagued our scientists since the mushroom cloud blossomed over Hiroshima in 1945. The problem, however, is twofold. Our politicians also must re-educate themselves in science to be able to properly frame their questions to the scientists who appear before the various Congressional committees. More importantly, perhaps, politicians must realize that scientists are not infallible.

During 1948—the year preceding the first Soviet atomic explosion—Oppenheimer and his fellow scientists continually assured the administration that the Russians could not achieve an atomic bomb until far in the future. They were wrong. At the same time, Vannevar Bush staked his reputation on the declaration that an intercontinental ballistic missile was "impossible" to build. He, too, was wrong.

As the scientists have not always been correct in their *technical* assessments, so likewise they have also faltered in their *social* and *political* judgments concerning the problems which scientific advances pose. As long as they remained in an advisory role, the scientists usually did not stir up any great controversy. It was only when they meandered into the whirlpool of policy making that they found themselves in troubled waters. AEC Chairman Glenn Seaborg has praised the development of advisory relationships between the scientists and Government. "Scientists are asked for advice; scientists offer advice," he said bluntly. "But the permeation of science into the whole fabric of our society requires that science be utilized other than as a reference book—other than a Noah Webster or a Dr. Spock or a Dr. Gesell. It means that science must become a *general* and *participating partner* in government, not merely a limited or advisory partner. Men who *know* science and technology—whether or not they are scientists or engineers—must join in creating our *laws,* in forming our social order and in establishing our national policy."

Seaborg further pointed out that, during our nation's founding and early development, we drafted lawyers into all three branches of Government service. "We still need the lawyer," he said, "but we must extend the draft to a new class. We must conscript science and technology. We can no longer afford to exempt the scientists and the engineers. We must reclassify him. We must convince him that there is as much challenge and excitement in the laboratories of government as in the laboratories of science."

Dr. Wallace Sayre, professor of public administration at Columbia University, coined a precise definition of the problem of technological experts in Government when he wrote: "Scientists influential in the creation, maintenance, and modification of American science policy are scientists in politics. Their spokesmen need not always be occupants of public office or party officials, but, whoever they are, they cannot escape politics and remain leaders of science. They will have to share all the hard knocks of the political process and the difficulties imposed upon those who attempt to shape public policy. They will sooner or later have to recruit allies from organized groups of nonscientists, since they will soon discover that they cannot exert a unilateral dominance in the formulation of science policy.

"As they move into alliances with other similar interest groups on the peace issue, etc., they will discover that a price will have to be paid in the form of a mutually acceptable compromise on policies and priorities." Sayre concluded with this warning: "It is time that the scientists who have been sternly lecturing the nonscientists about their need to understand science, in turn realize that they themselves have an obligation to understand politics."

The scientists' efforts to present their case to the public have too often been marred by their limited interests. Although such groups as the NAS, AAAS, FAS, and other have contributed on many occasions to public enlightenment, by failing to go far enough in taking strong, sound stands on controversial issues, they have not fulfilled their responsibilities to the community at large.

Scientists who wish to influence science policy in a democratic society must enter the political arena along with other lobbying groups. They cannot remain in an ivory tower above the turmoil. No single approach to their problems of plunging into politics will suffice for more than a very small segment of the scientific community. The activities of the various *ad hoc* scientific groups which arose to cope with separate problems like fallout and nuclear testing have usually been unsustained. Through these sporadic social protests, many scientists have made their voices heard for the first time beyond the confines of their laboratories.

In a December, 1961, address to a Phi Beta Kappa assembly, Dr. Harrison Brown said more scientists should become active in partisan party politics. "I wish that many scientists would select the political party which comes closest to their beliefs," he said, "and then work actively within that party. I personally took this step many years ago and have found it to be a most rewarding experience.

"It seems to me that if democracy is to thrive, it is important that our system of political parties be made to function as well as possible. This means that thinking people should become active in the political process, over and above the simple activity of voting. I have seen scientists contribute substantially to political programs by providing information which is helpful in the drafting of campaign positions and speeches. Persons who are candidates for office usually are appreciative of this help, as are the workers around them. Also, a two-way educational process takes place which is healthy. The politician learns something about the complexities of the political process."

In 1960, Vice-President Nixon was advised to make the main basis of his Republican presidential campaign the assertion that the full development of the United States depended on a national program of scientific and technological exploitation, to which he would devote his full energies if elected. The Republican platform stressed the importance of science to the nation. Unfortunately, the Republicans failed to put any scientists on their Committee on the Impact of Science and Technology. Their advisory group was composed of a medical doctor, two businessmen, a college administrator, two architects, and a radio broadcaster.

Back in 1958, a group of 20 scientists agreed to form an Advisory Committee on Science and Technology within the Advisory Council of the Democratic Party. The committee produced two major documents which were subsequently widely used by Democratic candidates and by party workers as background material.

One of the studies involved the problems of disarmament. The committee came forward with a specific proposal for the creation of a special agency within the executive branch to undertake the research and development that would be necessary if we were ever successfully to approach negotiations in this area.

The Democratic Advisory Committee on Science and Technology made a formal report, *Defense, Disarmament and Survival,* on December 27, 1959. The scientist-authors were not as worried over the decline of American technology as they were over the rapid upsurge of the U.S.S.R. and Red China.

The committee recommended five steps that could be taken in the military area to create a quasi-stable situation until an effective disarmament agreement could be made. These steps were: (1) Reduction of the vulnerability of our own retaliatory system; (2) Reduction of the vulnerability of our defensive system; (3) Improvement of our detection system to reduce the possibility of a false alarm; (4) Introduction of further safeguards against surprise attack; (5) A major effort, with the cooperation of the U.S.S.R., to slow down the rate of spread of nuclear and missile technology.

The advisory scientists also recommended that disarmament

be made a major national goal. They suggested the immediate establishment of a National Peace Agency—as an independent organization—within the executive branch, with a starting budget of $1 billion.

In the judgment of these scientists, the first step in the process of eliminating the possibility of a surprise attack would be a bilateral U.S.–U.S.S.R. agreement, setting limits to nuclear testing and establishing controls on which later abolishment of testing could be based. The report stressed that Red China should be involved in these negotiations—even though the U.S. had no official relations with that power.

*Defense, Disarmament and Survival,* approved by Senators Humphrey, Kennedy, and Symington; Governor Adlai Stevenson, former Secretary of the Air Force Thomas K. Finletter, and former President Harry Truman, became a plank in the 1960 Democratic platform. Defense and disarmament matters were brought up often during the campaign. Following President Kennedy's inauguration, the proposed peace agency legislation was introduced in Congress. After considerable debate and some modification, the United States Arms Control and Disarmament Agency was formally created.

After this first legislative triumph of the young Kennedy Administration, Dr. Harrison Brown concluded: "I would like to stress that had scientists not involved themselves in politics, had this group of men elevated their noses and stated that politics was beneath their dignity—or had they stated simply that they were too busy—we probably would not have a Disarmament Agency today. It is, I believe, a beautiful example of how citizens of good will and knowledge can function effectively and with dignity in the democratic process."

This episode also marked the first example in American politics of a group of scientists working together as a team to achieve a mutually agreed upon nonscientific goal. Previously, scientists had worked jointly only on predominantly scientific projects.

Glenn Seaborg, the 51-year-old AEC chairman, sees scientists as lawmakers "if we can find scientists who are willing to have a try at this mode of life and if we can find the scientists who have the necessary combination of what I call scientific and political capabilities." He says that he already knows several people who would fit his description, although he has politely hesitated to name them outright. He agreed that it "was important to convince them to run for office, because it would be very helpful" to have more people with deep training in science in Congress to serve on such committees as the Committee on Astronautics in the House and Senate and the Joint Congressional Committee on Atomic Energy.

Seaborg cautioned, however, that we should not emulate the Soviets "who have virtually enthroned the engineer and the scientist in the seats of power so that they number a *majority* of the members of the Presidium, the Council of Ministers, and the Party Secretariat. But we must bring the engineer and the scientist across the threshold and into the chambers where our national policy is created—not merely allow them to stand in the corridors where it is discussed. We can no longer afford to insulate the body politic from the contributions, influence, and impact of such a significant segment" of our society. He assumed that the scientists who take the plunge into Government service could acquire a sufficient degree of proficiency for success in the science of politics.

Dr. Herbert York, chancellor of the University of California at San Diego and former chief scientist for the Advanced Research Projects Agency and the Pentagon, agrees wholeheartedly with Seaborg that "a small fraction of the national Congress should consist of scientists and engineers." But he feels that scientists will probably find it hard to "persuade the electorate of any particular constituency that their particular problems, as opposed to the nation's general problems, would be better handled by a scientific representative." Most political leaders, according to York, are likely to believe "that they will best be served directly by someone who is known to be adept at something, which, for want of a better name, may simply be called 'politics.' They will prefer to have someone representing them who has a background in law or local political affairs."

York is also worried about the length of time that it would take an elected scientist senator or representative to become effective. He believes that this period might be so long that the frustrated scientist-legislator might get so out of touch with his original calling that "he would no longer be able to do the same kind of job he would have done had he not served in Congress." York believes that this problem would not be as serious for a scientist serving in an appointed post in the executive branch, since most of the time he would be involved largely with matters of science and technology.

Dr. Harold Urey, Nobel Prize winner for the discovery of heavy water, believes that a scientist or anyone else who has a desire to do so should run for political office, but he feels that scientists "are not likely to be good vote getters. Good scientists have too much the quality of being forthright, where many times in a political situation it is necessary not to say everything that one thinks."

The scientist who chooses to run for office to be a policy maker often finds himself fighting a rather lonely battle. Unfortunately, there is no large politically active group of scientists to which a scientist might go to seek political support. Leo Szilard's rather small Council for Abolishing War, which actively supported three Democratic Senatorial peace candidates in the 1962 election, has been the lone exception. The Federation of American Scientists tries to influence legislation but does not openly support anyone running for public office.

There have been recent rumblings that American scientists should become more active politically—both as officeholders and as lobbyists in the Congressional cloakrooms—because the time left to engineer man's survival on this planet is running out. These outcries have not come from the missile and space scientists and engineers, who for the most part are conservatively rooted to cold war weapons technology, and have not as yet felt free to criticize the hand that feeds them. Rather, it has been the older atomic scientists, like Szilard, Rabi, Seaborg, and Feld, who have taken the lead in urging scientists to increase their civic activity. Rabi, who teaches physics at Columbia, said recently that he would "like to see active political clubs in our great engineering schools where the issues of the day are debated by keen minds accustomed to inquiring why, accustomed to getting down to basic questions, and also oriented toward finding new methods and new solutions to new problems and old. If such activity interfered with the hard grind to which these people are ordinarily subjected," the Nobel laureate continued, "I would be prepared to lengthen the course of study or even to narrow its professional focus somewhat in order to gain general utility of the human material involved."

Rabi went on to say that "we have to dispel the notion that a man of science who devotes part or all of his time to some public office has somehow deserted a sacred cause for a field much less worthy of his talents." Although most contemporary scientists have shunned Government posts, except in wartime, Rabi pointed out that many scientific greats have served their countries long and well. Newton filled the post of Master of the British Mint with great distinction. Benjamin Franklin served his young country in numerous political capacities, including his ambassadorship to France and his participation in the framing of the Constitution.

"We have enough knowledge, when properly applied and integrated, for men to have a much deeper understanding of themselves, and to use the knowledge for transcendant purposes," Rabi said. "Yet the real possessors of this knowledge are in their studies, in their laboratories, seeking more and more information, more knowledge, and living apart from their fellow men while their destiny is being shaped by people who have little realization of the power of the tools at our command."

Rabi has made an important contribution with his suggestion that *all* science students in the colleges become more oriented to the political problems of the day. Whether they eventually decide to leave the laboratory or remain within it for the rest of their professional careers, the scientists of tomorrow would at least have the opportunity for a better grounding than their predecessors in the social, historical, political, and economic impacts of the new technology. In this respect, they might take a cue from the late eighteenth-century country squire of Monticello, Virginia.

Thomas Jefferson, our first and only scientist-President (Herbert Hoover was an engineer), believed the safeguard of freedom was the education of the individual. To Jefferson, science and mathematics were basic in training the mind for rational thinking. He himself was a semiprofessional botanist, paleontologist, archaeologist, astronomer, cartographer, meteorologist, geologist, mineralogist, horticulturist, mathematician, medical doctor, architect, and zoologist. No other President since Jefferson has understood science as well or done so much for it—relatively speaking. He promoted scientific agriculture, foresaw the potentials of steam power, and enthusiastically supported smallpox vaccination. His detailed instructions to Lewis and Clark showed his grasp of the importance of obtaining practical scientific knowledge about the West.

Obviously, no twentieth-century President can ever expect to become another all-around scientific Chief Executive in the Jeffersonian tradition because the immense increase in scientific knowledge since the turn of the eighteenth century has made it physically impossible for any man to become a specialist in, at the most, more than two or three scientific disciplines. But it is important for every politician, whether his eyes are set on the State House, the White House, or Congress, to become better acquainted with the general technological changes in the major sciences if he is not to be an ignorant and ill-informed citizen.

Jefferson left us a noble legacy on this point in a letter that he wrote to DuPont de Nemours in 1816: "Enlighten the people generally, and tyranny and oppressions of body and mind will vanish like evil spirits at the dawn of day." The mission that Jefferson outlined a century and a half ago remains the supreme challenge today.

# Chapter 16

# Is Scientific Freedom Being Threatened by Too Much Secrecy?

One of the perennial problems of Government interest in science is the corresponding encroachment in the realm of traditional scientific freedom. Because many scientists have not always paid heed to the social and political responsibilities of their profession, various limitations have crept in to hamper their traditional freedom in recent years.

This problem has become increasingly acute during the last 20 years. Dr. Seaborg, speaking recently of the dilemma of science and secrecy which confronted American scientists after World War II, had this to say: "Hopes of turning great gains made in the nuclear field toward the solution of major human problems of the postwar years were for awhile dimmed by fears for future security. The first legal framework creating an atomic energy program in the United States was a product of the disillusionment resulting from our futile efforts to secure international control and at the same time a recognition of the need for maintaining some degree of security in an uneasy world."

The depth of this pessimism is reflected in one of Dr. Conant's 1952 Bampton Lectures on Modern Science and Modern Man: "The world being what it is today and is likely to be for a long time to come, secrecy and applied nuclear physics are words that must be joined together.

"But," he goes on to say, "it is of the utmost importance that the general public understands the consequences of this union . . . . Advances in science are difficult within a secret

195

national monopoly because necessarily its research is guarded from all but a few branches of the government. Secrecy and science are fundamentally antithetic propositions."

"So wise a man as Conant proved too pessimistic in his judgment that restoration of freedom in nuclear science would be delayed indefinitely," Seaborg noted, in sketching the history of this problem. "Though encouraging prospects for international control were no less remote," Seaborg went on, "our conviction grew stronger that the United States must secure for itself and other well-intentioned nations the benefits of peaceful uses of nuclear energy—including the renewal of an open, as opposed to a restricted, system of scientific cooperation."

An early public statement of this new determination came in President Eisenhower's address to the U.N. General Assembly on December 8, 1953, when he proposed an Atoms for Peace Program and the establishment of an international agency to promote peaceful application of atomic energy. In the rapid developments that followed, plans were laid for the first Geneva Conference on the Peaceful Uses of Atomic Energy. Congress acted during the latter part of 1954 to pass the first complete revision of the statutory charter of the U.S. Atomic Energy Commission since its establishment in 1946. By this act, Atoms for Peace became the basic U.S. nuclear policy—but we still continued to stockpile thousands of thermonuclear weapons.

Despite this victory and partial opening of the security curtain, Seaborg was too optimistic concerning the lifting of the veil of secrecy that still hung over most of the Government's atomic and other scientific research and development projects.

In his timely book *Science in the Cause of Man*, Gerard Piel, publisher of the *Scientific American,* has written an excellent chapter on the strains in the political atmosphere which have endangered the growth of science in a democracy. He dramatically retells the story of the fruitless censorship policy adopted by the Government to prevent discussion of the H-bomb by his distinguished journal. The AEC actually burned

3,000 copies of the April, 1950, issue of the *Scientific American* because an article by Dr. Hans Bethe contained three paragraphs that AEC security officers felt should be deleted in the national interest.

Although the three paragraphs merely mentioned technical points that had been in the open literature of world physics since the 1930's, the AEC decided to roll back the pages of history. "The wisdom of Bethe and his colleagues," Piel declared, "was grounded in thermonuclear physics. No proper weight could be given to their counsel on the ethical, political and other headings if the public could not share their understanding of the technical aspects of the new weapon." Although the information in these three paragraphs has since been declassified, the magazine-burning incident marked only the beginning of a series of similar events in which scientific advances were suppressed "in the national interest."

Less than a month after the dramatic and tragic Oppenheimer–AEC security hearings were concluded in May of 1954, Representative R. Walter Riehlman of New York opened another set of hearings with his House Subcommittee on the Organization and Administration of Military R&D Programs. The brilliant AEC commissioner, Dr. John von Neumann, set the stage and tone of the investigation when he turned his testimony to the touchy and "more urgent problem of security." He said that this was "our *major* problem which is growing more serious as time goes on."

Von Neumann felt disturbed that the security problem was in a "legal no man's land," and that the public looked upon security proceedings as "minor trials for treason." He recommended that the security problem be transferred from the administrative to the judicial area by Congressional legislation. He pointed out that he was not talking as an "alarmist," but he believed that the relationship between the scientists and the military was being "damaged and endangered by recent developments."

Two days later, on June 17th, when Dr. Killian of M.I.T.

testified, he spoke in the same vein: "We must have a tight security system. . . . But I think we can go overboard on letting security stifle creative activities."

The next day, Vannevar Bush said the security system was "driving a wedge between the military and scientific people of the country and doing great harm." The partnership of the military and the scientist is "now almost destroyed," he commented sadly, "and one of the primary reasons is the security system."

Although all of these top scientists agreed that scientists under suspicion by their superiors do not make for progress, their testimony was in vain. In the two decades since their pleas to Congress for a relaxation of our tight security system, we have seen no sign that anyone in the executive branch took their advice. Under each succeeding President, the security cloak was pulled progressively tighter and tighter around all sensitive military and semimilitary programs. Even the forlorn scientific *Vanguard* earth satellite effort was "protected" from the public's probing eyes from 1956 to 1959 by a bureaucratic layer of 16 different executive security clearance agencies, each of which in turn had a hand in deciding what information could be declassified and released to the public on our first "peaceful" space effort.

On June 14, 1959, the late Democratic Senator Thomas Hennings of Missouri released some letters written to him as chairman of the Senate Constitutional Rights Subcommittee. The letters showed that 16 out of 17 Nobel Prize-winning American scientists had expressed varying degrees of fear that the Government's secrecy policy was retarding scientific progress. The Senator had sought the letters, he said, because of "numerous complaints that scientific development and progress in the United States have been seriously hindered by undue secrecy." (The only dissenter was Dr. William Murphy, a Boston physician, who won the prize for medicine in 1934. He felt that only a few physicists were the complainers.)

The overwhelming majority did not see it the way Dr. Murphy

did. Walter H. Brattain, a 1956 Nobel laureate, wrote: "It just does not make sense to classify fundamental scientific information. I feel very strongly that most restrictions which are done in the name of national security turn out to be foolish. A few restrictions well considered in special areas make a lot of sense. However, the tendency always is to allow such activities to expand."

Dr. Selman A. Waksman, who won the prize in 1952 for medicine, wrote that restrictions on the exchange of scientific information have a frightening effect on the scientific community, where the restraints are often considered wrong and unnecessary. "Besides frightening talent away," he said, "the restrictions often give shelter to the mediocre ones."

Finally, Fritz Lippman of the Rockefeller Institute and the 1953 winner for medicine and physiology, wrote that there is little to gain by imposing Government restrictions on information. "In a much worked upon field," he stated, "information will not remain secret for long, not because of leaks but because others will think in similar lines. This is how research works."

Senator Clinton P. Anderson, New Mexico Democrat, has been chairman of the Joint Committee on Atomic Energy for a number of years. He believes that our preoccupation with excessive classification in the atomic energy program—from "confidential" to "secret" to "top secret"—violates the public's basic right to know, and hobbles scientific advance. Although he conceded that in some instances secrecy is undeniably justified, the Senator also said that in others, "it would take a vivid imagination to determine a valid reason for putting the 'restricted data' tag on information."

He posed the question: "Is the secret stamp perhaps being used as a convenient shield behind which to hide information which someone somewhere happens not to like or not to agree with?"

He also pointed out that since World War II the AEC and the Department of Defense have held that secrecy is essential to national defense, while the press and other segments of the public fear that unnecessary secrecy is really obscuring the defense picture. He questioned whether it made sense to label something "top secret" and then release it in full to the press. The New Mexico lawmaker cited these several examples, where the press had printed extensive details of "classified" science projects before the projects had been declassified, or where the Government withheld information for an abnormally long period:

• *Project Argus*. The high-altitude nuclear explosions, conducted over the South Atlantic in 1958, were finally revealed in a front-page story in the New York *Times* on March 19, 1959.

• *The Strontium 90 Report*. This report, prepared by three Los Alamos scientists, told the results of the 1956 weapons tests. It was sent to the AEC on October 21, 1957, and was finally sent to Senator Anderson as "declassified" information on April 20, 1959. Yet, by the time he received the report—three years after the tests were conducted—there was a terse notation attached to the effect that the analysis was "somewhat out of date."

• *The "Scientist X" Affair*. This case pointed up the fallacy of unnecessary secrecy. Washington attempted to prevent any open discussion of the "restricted" Project *Rover* nuclear rocket program, while Los Alamos announced in the press the hiring of "Scientist X"—and described in detail the work that he would be doing on the project.

• *Project Sherwood*. A program instituted to control thermonuclear energy, *Sherwood* was classified by the AEC because of "divided opinion" among members of the American Physical Society who were secretly polled back on June 28, 1952, on whether they thought *Sherwood* should be classified "secret." The vote actually was 88 to 1 in favor of declassifying all research dealing with the use of thermonuclear forces to generate electric current, but the AEC decided that the *one* negative vote indicated a "division of opinion!" This single dissent, in the AEC's opinion, justified the secrecy ruling, even though the AEC's classification expert, who participated in the poll, voted *against* secrecy.

In the lower legislative branch of the Capitol another Congressman had been making similar startling discoveries. When the House Government Information Subcommittee was formed in 1955 under the dynamic chairmanship of Democratic Representative John Moss of California, it was quickly determined that the flow of scientific information was being impeded by two major obstacles. The first was the excessive secrecy which placed the American scientist in an informational strait jacket. The second obstacle was the mounting mass of published technical material.

After extensive hearings, Moss decided the problem of secrecy could be attacked swiftly and with immediate success by instituting three major reforms in our security system. These reforms could be accomplished largely by a stroke of the President's pen. The three positive actions suggested to correct past errors in our security system were: (1) Elimination of the cumbersome Government multiple-clearance system, which often involved several agencies simultaneously in clearance cases. (2) Elimination of the vague "need-to-know" requirement, which needlessly restricted qualified persons' access to classified information. (3) Elimination of the stubborn efforts of the defense establishment to classify the basic laws of nature.

After listening to the testimony of many distinguished scientific witnesses, the subcommittee's recommendations were adopted unanimously by the parent House Government Operations Committee and submitted to Congress in April, 1958. None of these three security-easing recommendations have as yet been carried out.

Moss agreed with Anderson that there should be a small tight ring of scientific military secrets surrounding our weapons systems. "But secrecy does not automatically guarantee national security," he pointed out. He went along with the scientists who had said that excessive secrecy could retard science, cheapen the security system, and hence weaken our defense.

The second, allied obstacle has been the delay in disseminating *unclassified* scientific information to the public because of the scientists' tradition of publishing their first reports in technical journals. This meant long delays of six to twelve months or longer before a scientific article reached print. (In the Soviet Union, many articles reach the public press within one month.)

The most promising approach to solve the problems caused by the rising tide of published scientific material is the use of electronic machines for translation and for searching out and retrieving information from all published data dealing with a specific scientific problem. The Massachusetts Institute of Technology and other institutions have been working on such machines, but under grave financial handicaps.

A group of Russian experts visited M.I.T. a few years ago and demonstrated a vast and superior knowledge in this field. When they offered to exchange their latest findings for ours— an exchange that apparently would have benefited us more than them—the House Subcommittee was informed that the deal couldn't be made because of restrictions imposed on M.I.T. by *our* Government. Dr. Lloyd Berkner put it this way in his testimony before the Subcommittee: "What I am afraid of is that someday we may have to fight a war with pieces of paper marked 'secret' rather than weapons and men who are ready to fight."

The Russians made a massive frontal assault—ahead of us— on the problem of how best to handle the growing accumulation of technical literature. In the early fifties, they organized the All-Union Institute of Scientific and Technical Information, with a trained staff numbering many times that of our own small Armed Forces Technical Information Agency. The Russians have an advanced system of machine translation and search of scientific information, while we sputter along with an apparent lack of official interest at high levels, reflected in a shortage of funds.

The U.S. armed forces finally came up with a production

model of an electronic technical articles translator in late 1962 —many years after the Soviets already had theirs in operation. But, as Congressman Moss put it: "I am afraid, based on the opinions of scientists acquainted with Russian progress, that this is another case of too little too late."

Unfortunately, many scientists outside of the Government are opposed to our imitating the Russians in the establishment of a Government information clearinghouse, for these scientists fear undue Federal restrictions. Many would prefer strengthening the present channels of communication by providing subsidies for abstracting and indexing services, and for existing technical journals (like the monthly Soviet space science supplement sponsored by the NSF in the *Journal of Aeronautics and Astronautics*). Other scientists feel that these steps will not be enough, however, to catch up with the Russian lead.

In December, 1962, the NASA Public Affairs Office forced a compromise solution to this problem after a dispute between the Public Affairs Office and scientists in the Space Science Division. The scientists wanted to withhold data on the successful *Mariner II*'s flight past Venus until it was published in the professional journals. Dr. George Simpson, the new NASA Director of Public Affairs, was able to wrangle a concession from the stubborn scientists to release their stories on the temperature, magnetic field, and radiation of our neighboring planet after their *acceptance* for publication, instead of on the *actual* publication date. In this way, the people heard the dramatic news about the scientific deep-space experiments near Venus months earlier than they would have if the scientists had had their way.

The freedom of scientific information has also been restrained in the Pentagon by the restrictive policies of President Eisenhower's reorganization order, which gave his Assistant Secretary of Defense for Public Information the power to control the dispensing of information for security reasons. Assistant Defense Secretary Murray Snyder edited news releases emanating from the Pentagon under Eisenhower on the basis of a vague directive called "timeliness." The Kennedy Administration's Pentagon news chief, Arthur Sylvester, put still another clamp on public information as a result of the Cuban crisis in the fall of 1962, and Americans lost another battle in their continual struggle for the right to know.

Sylvester's now famous remark that information was being used as "a weapon in our arsenal" was the final admission by a high Washington source that the generation of news (including scientific news) was in itself a part of the nation's defense system.

On this issue, Senator Anderson feels that we were justified in maintaining the secrecy surrounding our atomic energy program as long as we were the sole possessor of the atomic bomb. But now that secrecy "has become a habit," he says, "the question is whether or not it is being abused." He believes that the classification experts tend to be overconservative and to play it safe. Under the law, all atomic energy information is "born classified," so the burden of responsibility for disseminating nuclear information rests on those seeking to remove the classified tags.

"Classification should not be used," the Senator says, "to keep from the public information vital to health and safety . . . or to hide data that has no defense implications." He is concerned that the suppression of scientific information prevents discussion which might produce solutions to the problems at hand. "It is impossible to say how many scientific breakthroughs have perhaps been delayed—or even prevented—because scientists were not free to exchange information," he points out.

It is up to the scientists working in Government military and space projects to provide the leadership in breaking the security classification bottleneck placed on most of their recent technological advances. The present array of security clearance limitations has only hampered the free flow of ideas.

The Armed Forces Technical Information Agency (ASTIA) supplies at present a mere 1,900 companies with technical documents. The Department of Defense has proposed that the number of technical documents handled annually by ASTIA be increased to 300,000. This would not greatly help the situation, however, because this agency has resources to process only one half of the 30,000 documents it is now receiving annually.

A Government-imposed blackout of all privately financed research and development work excludes most of these R&D findings from the public domain. The general problem of merely trying to read the sheer mass of technical R&D data in journals, books, and reports is compounded by the fact that much of the material is indigestible, unselected, and unedited.

The lesson we can learn from this situation is that an organized effort is needed if we are to tap this Government R&D so that its benefits will spill over to civilian technology. But who will do it?

Three types of existing organizations could play an important part in harnessing space R&D for private uses. These are the Government, education, and industry. Unfortunately, the Pentagon has not yet recognized the advances of industrial R&D as part of its mission. "Their indifference to spill-over is intolerable," says Robert Solo of the National Planning Association.

Other agencies of the Government, such as the AEC and NASA, are interested in transmitting space R&D know-how to private industry. But the Government's industrial relations and patent policy is a hodgepodge. The best prototype Government organization for the systematic transmission of R&D results has been the Department of Agriculture. Fortunately, their data has been largely unclassified, so the security problem has not reared its ugly head in this area.

The future transmission of R&D for civilian consumption may be indirect, with applications of military R&D being integrated first into the general body of science and then carried to industry. The universities can provide a bridge between the specialized scientific disciplines, on the one side, and the Government and industry, on the other. It will require complex social engineering in the future to achieve the goal: making private enterprise a vital component of the Government R&D system.

Solo has listed three ways to accomplish this feat:

1. Similar items of space military technology must be identified and matched for transfer to civilian uses.

2. Research reports of R&D can be promulgated with an eye to possible special needs of industry.

3. Essential scientific and technical breakthroughs in space R&D should be announced in terms meaningful to the businessman.

The transmission of this information is a two-way process, for our economic growth does not depend so much on our capacity to generate scientific advance as on our capacity to respond to it. The present scientific know-how of America and Europe is available to Africa, Latin America, and Asia. But no American company has yet sent to the National Atomic Laboratory at Oak Ridge an executive team that can be compared with the competition-minded and thorough teams of visiting Japanese. "American businessmen have told AEC officials that they learned most about nuclear technology from foreign teams who visited them after they had made AEC tours," Solo says. Japanese and West German companies buy as many AEC publicly advertised engineering drawings and instruments as do American companies!

In November, 1961, the AEC's 90 repository libraries in the United States received 124 requests for copies of their unclassified documents, whereas the 90-odd AEC libraries abroad received a total of 518 requests. But the AEC was not the only large Government agency with a problem of finding improved means of disseminating scientific information to the consumer. The Pentagon and NASA were constantly being bombarded with requests to share the wealth of their R&D findings with American industry.

In a speech made before a National Security Industrial Association symposium in March, 1963, John Rubel, assistant secretary of defense for research and engineering, acknowledged that the bulk of original thinking and facilities for accomplishing R&D still comes from industry without which the revolutionary developments in weapons would not have been possible. He said he hoped that the Association could be of help in improving the utilization of manpower resources, the application of new knowledge and techniques on a broader scale, and improving communications between the Government and privately supported segments of the national R&D effort. Then he warned his listeners:

"The rate at which government support of research and development has increased in recent years cannot go on forever. . . . It is obvious that a vast segment of industry does not share directly and probably shares very little even indirectly in the techniques and the approach to problems which have stemmed and are stemming from the military space program that account for the bulk of federally supported R&D.

"It is clear, also, that these R&D expenditures often serve comparatively narrow purposes. They may be, and hopefully in all important cases they are, necessary purposes. But although necessary, they may, from a national standpoint, be more costly than we have tended to realize. The purposeful broadening of the objectives that are served by federally supported research and development activities would appear to be clearly in the national interest, and certainly in the national security interest."

During the same week, NASA appointed Walter L. Lingle to the newly created post of Deputy Associate Administrator for Industrial Relations to help speed up the flow of technical information to industry. This move and Rubel's speech were refreshing signs of new attempts within the Government not only to break the classification barriers but to share the fruits of R&D with civilian companies.

To help solve the problem of how best to handle the burgeoning Government problem of the dissemination of scientific information, the National Science Foundation established its

Office of Science Information Service in 1959. This office, set up as a result of a PSAC recommendation, had been operating rather limply—because of a shortage of funds and its struggle with the security problem—to promote better coordination of scientific information activities within the Federal government. Although the NSF has made some progress in the dissemination of information, it has, according to Dr. Wiesner, "achieved only limited success in developing a coordinated national scientific information system, since it has no administrative authority over other agencies."

In May, 1962, the Federal Council on Science and Technology recognized this problem and recommended that a high-level focal point of responsibility should be established within each Government agency to integrate and elevate the status of science information. The Council also appointed a committee to develop Government-wide standards on scientific and technical information. Much work still remains to be done in this area before any worth-while results can be achieved and the classification bottleneck can be broken.

On February 17, 1963, a group of scientists concerned with the over-all technical communications problem formed a new organization to provide the public with objective, understandable scientific information bearing on public policy issues. The new organization, called the Scientists Institute for Public Information, is the first of its kind in America.

Secrecy prevents the formation of an informed public opinion. The blackout curtain of secrecy has often shrouded the facts the American people need so they can exert their proper influence in the formulation of major democratic policy decisions. "The force of misinformed public opinion," Senator Anderson has stated, "could well lead to establishment of policies detrimental to the national security. In any case, the dissemination of 'half-facts'—which is now all too prevalent—can lead only to utter confusion."

To solve the secrecy problem we must break the habit of secrecy, which has increasingly pervaded our Government agencies, and form new habit patterns. The burden of proof should be placed on those responsible for placing the classified stamp on Government science information rather than on those seeking it. Because Government security officers have not used their powers with caution, the improper and indiscriminate use of the "secrecy" label has already undermined our entire security structure.

Until the scientists, through their professional organizations, make a greater effort to help set public policy which has scientific implications, and until they more actively combat the insidious tentacles of the "secrecy" myth, they will be abdicating a precious right of democracy.

## Chapter 17

# What Should Be the Government's Role in Science Education?

The demand for increased quality and quantity of university trained scientists has come in the wake of the phenomenal growth of Big Science. Since *Sputnik,* the cry that Russia is graduating two scientists to our one has been constantly in our ear.

The passage of the National Defense Education Act (NDEA) in 1958 was an attempt to answer this cry by providing direct Federal aid in the form of loans and grants for teaching science, mathematics, and foreign languages in public and private schools and colleges throughout the nation. Despite the millions of dollars appropriated for laboratory equipment, textbooks, and science workshops in the five years since the passage of the NDEA, the gap between Soviet and American scientific education still yawns alarmingly wide.

Several problems surrounding the expansion of Government aid to science education and research need further exploration before adequate solutions can be achieved. Questions like the following spotlight a few of these problems.

• What happens to the academic freedom of the colleges as more Federal money is pumped in to shore up lagging science research and teaching?

• How can more money be channeled into basic research and less for applied research in our universities?

• How far should the government go in subsidizing higher education for our future scientists?

- How can we bring the engineers and scientists closer together in their training?
- How do we bring these two groups closer to the social scientists?
- How can science and education best help the emerging, ex-colonial nations?
- How can our colleges broaden the scientific curriculums so that the students will become more politically minded?

Professor Barry Commoner of Washington University, St. Louis, predicts that the space agency will require the services of one in every four United States scientists by 1970. Commoner called this a "spectacular balancing act—education supported by science, science by space, and space by the man on the moon," and he asked: "Will it work?" The answer of the critics is a worried "No." With the talented scientific cream—and perhaps most of the milk—skimmed off each year, they believe that other scientific tasks will suffer. What can be done to alleviate this fear?

While he was still chancellor of the University of California, Dr. Glenn Seaborg headed a PSAC panel to investigate this very problem of the Federal government's role in basic research and graduate education. In its November 15, 1960, report to the President entitled *Scientific Progress, the Universities and the Federal Government,* the panel said the record of the United States in basic research and graduate education was one not of failure. They declared that American science was "second to none" in the world, because, in part, of the highly constructive role the Federal government had played in supporting it.

The panel did see fit, however, to make some general recommendations aimed at improving the educational aspects of science in America. They urged that (1) all parts of the national community assume greater responsibility for supporting scientific R&D for the national welfare; (2) more support be given science by doubling the number of universities experimenting in basic R&D during the next 15 years; (3) communion be achieved between the education of scientists and basic research; (4) quality of college instruction be improved and more energy be devoted to new fields of research by the Federal, state and local governments.

The panel further recommended that universities pay proper salaries, modernize science on the graduate level, include experience both in research and teaching for their staffs, and accept primary responsibility for insuring that their growing partnership with Government will reinforce their freedom and excellence—not undermine them. The scientists also suggested greater Federal support for basic research, fellowships, and graduate education. Once the money is granted, the report urged that the Government not seek to supervise the projects.

But few of these recommendations will be realized unless their pressing needs can be fulfilled at the same time.

Dr. Theodore von Kármán, the late dean of U.S. aerospace scientists, has pointed out that without engineers there would be no real scientific progress. "This is a great problem of education," he said philosophically, "because we really need all the physicists, chemists and others, but we also really need the creative [engineering] people—not the inventors, there will always be inventors—who will create hardware. And it is not a shameful thing to create hardware. How the technical universities will solve this is not clear to me." Von Kármán was a living symbol of the attempt to bring scientists and engineers into a closer working relationship. Unfortunately, there have been too few scientist-administrators of his abilities in Government posts.

"Today the picture of the scientists in the public mind is a confused triple exposure which includes the images of the scientist, the engineer, and the technician," Dr. Killian told an M.I.T. centennial audience in 1961. "Science is not space vehicles, nor rockets, nor miracle drugs, nor nuclear weapons."

Warren Weaver wrote in the *Report of the Commission on National Goals:* "Science is not a trivial business of tricky hardware, not the phony bubbling retorts of the advertisements, not strange men with white coats or beards, but the response, at once poetic and analytical, of man's creative mind to the challenge of the mystery of matter and life."

It is science in this sense that we need to understand and to emphasize as an integral part of our culture. Viewing and understanding science in this way, we have a better chance to carry the meaning of science to the awakening peoples, and, with them, gain new confidence in the capacity of intelligence to build a better world.

Even though scientists and engineers, growing closer in knowledge, methods, and work, are finding their domains increasingly overlapping, the role of the engineer remains distinct and importantly differentiated. He applies the concepts and discoveries of the scientists to the practical needs of the human community: its health, prosperity, and individual fulfillment. He is far more than a technician. He fulfills a social role vital to our society.

Dr. John Hrones, vice-president of Case Institute of Technology for Academic Affairs, comments on this point: "The great engineering achievements of the past decade are always attributed to the scientists and the role of the engineer is never delineated. The development of the atomic submarine, and the development of satellites and space probes are always spoken of as scientific achievements when, in reality, they are major engineering accomplishments. True enough, science unlocked important secrets of nature to make them possible, but yet, the real achievement has been an engineering one."

During World War II, many of the developments in fields such as radar and nuclear energy were inherently engineering in character. Sadly, only a handful of our engineers knew enough about the scientific advances to exploit them. Therefore, science and engineering of necessity became intermingled in a new breed of engineers, some physicists and chemists who had absorbed engineering knowledge—and engineers from various backgrounds who became knowledgeable in nuclear physics and chemistry. The best qualification for the new tasks was a thorough knowledge of the basic principles of mathematics, physics, and chemistry. An engineer who understood the basic principles of heat transfer could apply them to the cooling of a radar transmitter tube . . . a reactor fuel element . . . or even a satellite and its equipment in the space environment. Thus, less specialization and a greater integration of the basic scientific principles underlying all engineering applications became the essential for survival in a rapidly changing world.

Since even professional groups use the term *scientist* for both scientists and engineers, it is not surprising that the public has difficulty in comprehending the dual aspect of the research and development process, and the diversity of talents required at opposite ends of the spectrum. The purpose of the *scientist* is "to know and understand nature, to bridge the gap between the known and the unknown," according to Dr. Hrones, who goes on to define the purpose of the development *engineer* as the applying of the "resources of nature for social ends, to bridge the gap between the known and the desired."

The heavy emphasis on engineering in the space sciences and the location of most of our "true" scientists in the universities— outside Government and industry—has kept wide the gap between these two members of the same technical team. The need to weld these two groups into *one* smoothly functioning team able to cooperate for a decade or more on one space project is still one of the great unsolved problems of the Space Age.

Despite all the Federal money pumped into college science, education, and research in recent years, some disturbing facts were brought to light by a Brookings Institution study in October, 1962. The 36-college study made for the U.S. Office of Education concluded that the expenditure of Federal funds for science research and fellowships in our universities had failed to increase the proportion of students enrolling in the sciences. The report warned against harmful side effects, such as the overstress on research at the expense of teaching. At the level of undergraduate laboratory instruction in some universities, the study showed, fewer young scientists expressed a willingness to spend their time solely in teaching. The result was that "those who do [teach] are not highly regarded by their professional colleagues," the report said.

There is immediate need for an improved mechanism to provide leadership, guidance, and policy guidelines for an over-all Federal approach in support of the educational community. In response to this need, an *ad hoc* committee presided over by Commissioner Sterling McMurrin of the U.S. Office of Education met in May, 1962. Waterman of the NSF, Webb of NASA, Wiesner of the Office of Science and Technology, and Seaborg of the AEC were prominent committee members. All those present were interested in coordinating educational efforts and helping to make the National Defense Education Act work. This gathering marked another important step toward closer coordination between science, education, and the Government.

Seaborg is opposed to having a single Federal agency administer all educational programs. "Each agency," he argues, "should examine its own needs and consider supporting educationally oriented programs that are related to its over-all mission. However, each agency should not automatically be permitted to then establish, or indefinitely continue, its own educational programs. Rather, some central group, perhaps the U.S. Office of Education in the humanities and social sciences and the Office of Science and Technology in the engineering, and in the life and physical sciences, should exercise the responsibility of examining each agency's programs in relation to the total Federal effort."

As long as we do not have a Department of Science, the NSF will undoubtedly continue to originate policy proposals and recommendations concerning the support of basic research and education in the sciences; and the new OST will look to the Foundation to provide studies and information on which sound national policies in science and technology can be based.

It would appear that the Office of Science and Technology provides a central point for the coordination of all Federal science research efforts; the National Science Foundation is responsible to the OST in matters relative to science education and basic research; the Commissioner of Education has a responsibility for over-all coordination of all Federal educational activities; and the specialized agencies such as the AEC, NASA, and National Institutes of Health, Public Health Service, have the prerogative of administering educational activities in areas of their special interest but need to look for central guidance elsewhere.

The Atomic Energy Commission's educational assistance program embraces both research and educational support, since indeed graduate education and research cannot be divorced. The AEC makes grants to universities for laboratory equipment; awards fellowships in nuclear science, engineering, health physics, industrial hygiene, and industrial medicine; supports college and high school faculty institutes in radiation biology; and collaborates with the American Society for Engineering Education to support institutes in reactor technology for engineering faculties. Temporary staff appointments provide many opportunities for students and teachers to participate in research projects at the major AEC sites. This many-faceted commission also fosters curriculum development programs in nuclear science education. Research projects at universities and colleges are AEC-underwritten to the extent of $25 million annually.

Dr. Hugh Dryden, deputy administrator of NASA, told a group of college administrators at the first NASA-University Conference on the Science and Technology of Space Exploration in November, 1962, "It has been estimated that by 1970 as many as one-fourth of the nation's scientific and engineering manpower will be engaged in space activities. The university alone is the producer of this talent and, like the logger who has the responsibility of replacing for the future the trees which he harvests, NASA, as a user of university-trained talent, has an obligation to carry a fair share of the load of replacing the resources consumed."

To accomplish this task, NASA has set as a goal the yearly support of 4,000 doctoral candidates at 150 universities—a program that should annually yield 1,000 new Ph.D.s in space-related fields. Over $40 million of the NASA fiscal 1962 budget was allocated to academic institutions, of which $28 million was earmarked for project research. The fiscal 1963 program sees a doubling of this total university program. NASA, which has continually found itself woefully short of skilled manpower despite an expensive recruitment program, hopes its Sustaining University Program to encourage scientific and engineering training will end its personnel shortage.

Not all the top NASA executives are in favor of this program, as some of them feel that it is beyond the intended scope of the space agency. These critics feel that the program could be better administered by the NSF, the traditional source of governmental support of academic research and graduate studies in science and engineering. This division of opinion within NASA as to who should sponsor the program is far less important than the complete agreement of top space agency officials that the Government has a duty to subsidize scientific educational activity.

There thus appears to be an excellent framework upon which to build a Federal approach to support of education, *if* relatively uniform policy guidelines and fairly clear lines of demarcation between individual agencies and their programs are established. The time is ripe to benefit from this framework by taking certain positive steps outlined in plans now being developed by the Office of Education and outside sources.

But Dr. Alvin Weinberg, among others, has warned that Federal support of Big Science can ruin our universities by converting university professors into administrators, housekeepers, and publicists. Already, Federal expenditures for university research amount to one fifth of the total university budgets. This ever-growing percentage will powerfully affect the future course of our institutions of higher learning.

Dr. Lee DuBridge, president of Cal Tech, agrees with Weinberg that the chief threat of control over the universities where the Government has provided research funds, comes not from the panels and advisory committees—composed largely of professors—who must pass upon projects and budgets before any work can begin, but from the ulterior motives of those who select the members of the panels. DuBridge offered no solution to this problem of insidious control. Since someone has to pass on such requests, maybe a better method of panel selection is needed.

Because there is no turning back the clock to the "good old days," scientists and Government educators must learn to live together harmoniously. A bold approach is obviously and imperatively needed to improve the organizational and liaison relationships between Government agencies interested in science educational activities and the universities, secondary, and elementary schools of the nation. Various solutions to the problem have been advanced from both Government and private circles.

As former head of a major university (the University of California), Seaborg has come forward with a practical approach to solve this broad government-science problem.

He recommended the establishment of a permanent educational coordination committee chaired by the OST working with the NSF and the Office of Education to set up guidelines for interagency coordination; the development of fairly uniform Federal policies by interagency coordinating committees in fellowship and research areas; and the establishment by the Office of Education of joint agency efforts to carry out the science education programs of NASA, AEC, and NSF. Seaborg further felt that the Office of Education should play a more dynamic role by: (1) developing a specific Federal policy to aid technical institutes in community junior colleges; (2) endeavoring to improve science teacher training; (3) instituting a complete review of high school science curricula, rather than a piecemeal study of individual subjects; (4) establishing institutes and fellowships for college and high school faculties in the social sciences and humanities, modeled after the programs of the Oak Ridge Nuclear Laboratory and NSF; (5) considering the potentials of establishing either an optional or compulsory two-year science curriculum for nonscience college majors; (6) supporting vocational education and technician training for the retraining of workers replaced by technological advances; (7) improving communications among Federal agencies and the educational community at large.

A remarkable achievement in the improvement of high school science education began in 1961 when some 50,000 selected secondary school students in the United States started getting a coherent and modern fundamental introduction to physics through a new course prepared by the Physical Science Study Committee under the leadership of M.I.T. Professors Jerrold Zacharias and Francis Friedman. Motivated by a desire to make science really part of our culture, this program represents a major advance in science teaching. This was also the first time a unified approach to a *single* subject had been made available from the Federal level to all 50 states. The programs include a whole new battery of interrelated teaching materials— textbook, movies, newly designed experiments and laboratory equipment, and a wide range of collateral reading. "The spirit and methods generating in this new program are now spreading, with the chemist, the biologist, and the mathematician all developing new courses, with first-rate scientists and first-rate teachers from universities and secondary schools joining in the work," according to Killian. "Another group would like to work on grammar school science, and now the American Association of Physics Teachers is initiating a similar effort to improve college physics. Altogether, what the Physical Science Study Committee has produced and inspired may well represent a revolutionary approach to upgrading, deepening, and enriching the substance, the taste, and the cultural content of science teaching. The implications are profoundly important; yet the funds available to continue such efforts are exceedingly difficult to come by. For a small increase in expenditures for this purpose dramatic improvements can well be achieved in the quality of education," he concluded.

The British scientist and man of letters C. P. Snow, in his book *The Two Cultures and the Scientific Revolution,* presents an ambitious solution to the problem of helping the world's underdeveloped nations. In this volume Snow asserts: "To help the scientific revolution in the poor countries we will have to provide trained scientists and engineers adaptable enough to devote themselves to a foreign country's industrialization for at least ten years out of their lives. Here, unless and until the Americans and we educate ourselves both sensibly and imaginatively, the Russians have a clear edge. This is where their educational policy has already paid big dividends. They have such men to spare if they are needed. We just haven't, and the Americans aren't much better off. Imagine, for example, that the U.S. government and ours had agreed to help the Indians carry out a major industrialization, similar in scale to the Chinese. Imagine that the capital could be found. It would then require something like ten thousand to twenty thousand engineers from the U.S. and here to help get the thing going. At present, we couldn't find them."

The end of colonialism was seen as the greatest barrier to our expanding space effort by Dr. von Kármán, who felt that the 48 new nations with their low technical level of competence might slow down the progress of the more advanced nations. To achieve real international cooperation, we will have "to expend a certain amount of our energy, which we would otherwise use in our space program, to bringing up the technical level of these countries," he believed.

In the summer of 1961, a group of teachers and leaders from Africa and other countries, under the leadership of Professor Zacharias of M.I.T., took a hard fresh look at the possibility of new methods and concepts for teaching science in tropical Africa. This bold and difficult assignment was a heartening demonstration of the new will to leapfrog over the current pedestrian forms of education and achieve fundamental new approaches to science teaching—even for those environments where there is no science tradition.

In a number of our universities, engineering and science students and political science and public administration students are being brought together to study the ways in which their domains have penetrated each other. Dr. Killian of M.I.T. believes that "more general adoption of such courses of study at the interface between science and political science will eventually build more effective bridges of understanding and communication between those who pursue a career in science and those who pursue a political career." He hopes that it will yield more scientists who are both qualified and willing to enter public life.

Dr. Seaborg, first scientist to become chairman of the AEC after a succession of nonscientist administrators—including David Lilienthal, Lewis Strauss, and John McCone—believes that in addition to increasing the political awareness of our science students, the reverse side of the coin is equally important. He feels that we must develop a college course in science for the nonscience students.

"In addition to raising the science content of liberal education," he stated recently, "there are other measures that can be taken, I believe, to rectify the imbalance. Something can be done in the development of the academic departments. In the history department, for example, should there not be one or more historians with a special knowledge of and interest in science? On the political science faculty, I visualize a role for one or more men especially knowledgeable about the extensive effects of science on Government policy in domestic and international affairs. At a time when human thought has been undergoing a revolution, through the works of Einstein and Bohr and Hoyle, should not a department of philosophy have one or more men with strong ties to modern science? Considering the impact of science and technology on society, would it not be wise to have professors of sociology and social welfare who devote special attention to those interrelationships?

"Similarly," he added, "I wonder if there is not merit in giving some appointments in the science departments to men with special interests in the arts, the humanities, and the social sciences."

If better avenues of peace are to be explored, there is an obvious need for a closer working relationship between the natural scientists and the social scientists. Such relatively new organizations as the Society for Social Responsibility in Science and the Federation of American Scientists are but two of the organizations now quietly working to bridge the traditional gulf between the two broad science disciplines.

We need a new crop of civil servants in Washington who can communicate with both scientists and politicians, and serve the nation as the intellectual brokers between these two realms of our culture. A broadening of the humanities and the social sciences in our universities, as well as courses in the social appreciation of science, are necessary if men are to be educated for this role.

Early in 1963, the Kennedy Administration attempted to bring support for science and education together by tying its proposal for a massive Federal aid program for colleges and universities into its space and defense efforts. This move was made to avoid many previous Congressional objections to granting direct aid to schools. Legislation was drafted to implement the school-aid recommendations in the President's Science Advisory Council report, which read in part: "Impending shortages of talented, highly trained scientists and engineers threaten the successful fulfillment of vital national commitments."

McGeorge Bundy, presidential assistant for national security matters, found himself in the center of a storm of protest from fellow Princeton alumni when a reprint of his speech delivered before the American Council of Education in Chicago on October 4, 1962, appeared in the *Princeton Alumni Weekly* in February, 1963. His article coincided with Kennedy's new $5 billion omnibus bill for Federal subsidies to higher education—a bill already under fire on many college campuses throughout the nation. Bundy's article pointed out that over half of the university's current budget of $44 million for undergraduate and postgraduate education was supplied by research contracts with the Federal government.

He credited the "present level of achievement of the quantity and quality of American science" mainly to university contracts with the Government. In his article, titled "The Blessing That Is Federal Aid," Bundy asserted that constricting controls of education were totally absent from the university-Government contracts. Judging from the vigor of the nearly unanimous protests published in subsequent issues of the weekly, Bundy's fellow alumni didn't agree. The university had historically protected its academic independence by relying on private financing, predominantly by loyal alumni. But that picture has been changed drastically in recent years by huge Federal outlays, mainly for science and engineering, including the construction and nonacademic staffing of the Forrestal Research Center with its $2 million annual budget.

The protesting alumni feared the steady Federal encroachments on the freedom of those universities whose ideas were approved by the Washington planners in Baghdad-on-the-Potomac.

The best-known participant in the alumni uprising objected on different grounds, however. "You would hardly expect a socialist," he wrote, "who by no means objects to the principle of Federal aid . . . to protest at this point. And I am quite persuaded that the Federal government . . . keeps hands off the scientists . . . charged with carrying out this research. . . . But I think certain questions should be answered in understandable terms . . ."

Among the more pertinent questions he posed were these:

"To what extent do they generally tie in the universities to the military-industrial complex which President Eisenhower warned us against . . . [to the] prospect of the nation's scholars being tied to Federal employment, project allocation and the power of money?

"I found no reassurance in the speech by the former Dean of Harvard [Bundy] who now ornaments the Kennedy Administration."

The letter was signed Norman Thomas of the Princeton Class of 1905 and six times Socialist Party candidate for the presidency of the United States.

Bundy was irate when he read the protests and tried to

clarify the misunderstandings in a letter of explanation to senior Washington columnist Arthur Krock, who broke the original story in the New York *Times*. Bundy's apology was based on a change in title of his original speech ("Of Winds and Windmills"), and his feeling that the alumni misinterpreted his remark that, although Government supports carry some risk of limitations on the freedom of academic life, "we must give up our traditional fear of government money on these research projects."

Where Government money supporting R&D in the university laboratory furthers programs close to the university's goals, it contributes to the public service responsibilities of higher education. But where Washington forces the universities to deviate from the pursuit of science for science's sake, then the purity of higher education is sacrificed. If, as Seaborg and others believe, the concept of liberal education for all—and not just science education for *some*—is to play the key role in the future survival of our nation, then we need to broaden the scope of our thinking. We must find out what remains to be accomplished to achieve this cherished goal.

In its White House report of November, 1960, the PSAC's education panel recommended to the President: "Whether the quantity and quality of basic research and graduate education in the United States will be adequate or inadequate depends primarily upon the Government of the United States. From this responsibility the Federal government has no escape. Either it will find the policies—and the resources—which permit our universities to flourish and their duties to be adequately discharged—or no one will."

This is the supreme educational challenge to both science and the Government today—and tomorrow!

## Chapter 18

## How Can We Increase the Prestige
## of Our Scientists in Politics?

In recent years, the prestige of our top scientists has been enhanced by an increasing national recognition of their contributions to our society. Seven prominent American scientists have received the AEC's annual $50,000 Enrico Fermi Award, first authorized in 1954. The recipient of each year's award is decided by joint agreement of the commission and the President. The list of recipients is impressive: Enrico Fermi, John von Neumann, Ernest O. Lawrence, Eugene Wigner, Glenn Seaborg, Hans Bethe, and Edward Teller.

After Dr. Teller received the Fermi Award in 1962, J. Robert Oppenheimer's friends renewed their pressure on the Kennedy Administration to have the name of the former A-bomb director cleared. In October, 1961, the Federation of American Scientists sent to the AEC a letter asking for a complete review of the Oppenheimer case. AEC Chairman Seaborg, who worked with Oppenheimer on the Manhattan Project, was in favor of taking such steps. At an April 29, 1962, White House dinner honoring forty-nine Nobel Prize winners, Seaborg approached Oppenheimer on his feeling about another hearing. Oppenheimer had been invited to the dinner as a "trial balloon"—to test public reaction.

The rest of the administration was confronted with the dilemma of finding a proper way to "clear" Oppenheimer without reopening the hearings and subjecting him to another round of interrogation. Late in the spring of 1962, there was general agreement within the Kennedy inner circle that it would be a mistake to act then—since it would make the Oppenheimer case an issue in the coming fall Congressional elections.

But Wiesner, Seaborg, and others pressed for immediate action. Late in March of 1963, the General Advisory Committee of the AEC (which Oppenheimer headed during World War II) voted unanimously to present the 1963 Fermi Award to their former chief. On March 25th, the five-man AEC also unanimously approved the recommendation and passed their final decision on to the White House. President Kennedy announced the award to the nation on April 5th. It was hoped that this high honor, which would be presented officially on December 2, 1963, the 21st anniversary of the first nuclear chain reaction, would clear the way for eventual security clearance to Dr. Oppenheimer.

The lapse of time had indeed erased the bitter and personal political scars created nearly a decade earlier. Now the martyred physicist could receive the justified high honor for his "contributions to the development of nuclear energy" without further recriminations. The Government award symbolically removed the "security risk" tarnish that had covered this tragic figure of American science for so long. The Fermi Award also marked a symbolic turning point, for it sharpened the slow rise of the scientists' prestige curve, which had plummeted during the McCarthy era.

An even more significant award was presented to the 82-year-old dean of American scientists, Hungarian-born Dr. Theodore von Kármán, by President Kennedy on February 18, 1963. In a ceremony held in the White House Rose Garden, the Chief Executive pinned the first National Medal of Science on this pioneer "for his incomparable contributions not only to the fields of applied mechanics, aerodynamics, and astronautics, and to education in general, but also to industrial, national, international and human affairs in the broadest sense."

The idea for this award originated in the House Space Committee in 1959 and was authorized by Congress "for leadership in science and engineering." Von Kármán epitomized the new technical experts who successfully combine the science and engineering disciplines. This award signaled a change in attitude by the White House, which just five years earlier had disdainfully labeled the space scientists "eggheads." (In fact, the one presidential dinner given them after *Sputnik* was so painful to President Eisenhower that the experiment was not repeated for the remainder of his term of office.)

These awards place high national importance on the technical achievements so essential to keeping the arteries of our new national scientific vitality from hardening prematurely. So far, however, the few such awards have gone largely to the older scientific leaders who are nearing the end of their public careers. There is still little national recognition of the younger scientists, and the Nobel science awards unfortunately usually go to laboratory researchers, not to engineers or administrators. Therefore, other steps must be taken if these younger outstanding servants of society are to receive their just rewards.

Our scientists need to broaden themselves beyond the confines of their laboratories and the limits of their specialized disciplines in order to become more responsible citizens. In this way they can provide a democratic sequel to the story told about the high Air Force officer who on seeing his first atomic explosion remarked: "My God, the long-hair scientists have done it! Now we'll have to take it [the A-bomb] away from them!"

Distinguished sociologist Robert K. Merton has analyzed why so many scientists have been able to continue working in their ivory research towers uncontaminated by the social controversy that surrounds them. In his *Social Theory and Social Structure,* Merton wrote: "The intensified division of labor has become a splendid device for escaping social responsibility. . . . Each group of specialists finds it increasingly possible to pass the buck for social consequences of their work on the assumption that in this complex transferral of responsibility, there will be no hindmost for the devil to take."

This attitude is the underlying reason why so many scientists —and engineers in particular—have taken a conservative view toward supporting new uses for their inventions. As Harrison Brown has pointed out, the majority of scientists working for the Government during and after World War II felt that "weaponry was a way of life," and only a small minority have as yet broken away from this belief.

Besides the typical scientist's reluctance to venture from the protection of ivory towers, other reasons can be found why the drawbridge of greater scientific prestige has not been lowered over the moat between scientists and the public. Chief among these are the perennial and largely self-imposed organizational problems which have restrained scientific progress.

Dr. Simon Ramo, one of the nation's foremost missile experts, has pointed out on many occasions that "arrangement-making" and not "technological lag" is the big bottleneck to more rapid national progress. He notes that we have suffered as much from "not stopping" on a project as from "not starting new ones." The former problem is particularly acute where the politician is concerned, because, once a project gets too big, it is almost impossible to cancel it, even when it becomes obsolete, because of the economic dislocations that would surely result.

Ramo has come around to believe we need more social scientists to handle the increasing imbalance between technological and social advance. "We need more people who have a feel for people," he said, implying that they were not to be found in great abundance among the engineers.

One of the keys to greater progress in science is better organization of technical meetings as well as better administrative organization within the groups themselves. Many national and international scientific conferences are planned and controlled by the wrong people. Either the nonscientific bureaucrats, who run the various governmental and nongovernmental science organizations, or the so-called elderly scientific-statesmen, who have long ceased to do any significant scientific research, too often dominate these conclaves. Since modern science is a young man's game, it is time that more members of the new generation got out of their laboratories and took a more active part in breaking the barriers around the semi-closed meetings run by their elders.

Such a shift will necessitate the training of a new type of scientific administrator. Peter Kapitza, director of the Soviet Academy of Sciences, says the administrators of organized science should be the scientists themselves. He pointed to Ernest Rutherford as the first modern example of this new type of dual creature. Not only a great atomic scientist, Rutherford is also the creator and manager of a noted laboratory.

In America, we have a parallel example in AEC Chairman Glenn Seaborg. But for every Seaborg and Wiesner, we have a Waterman, Hagen, Dryden, or a Bronk—men not trained to be administrators, who usually slow up progress in their agencies by not being able to keep their fast-moving, scientifically oriented ships on a steady course.

One of the underlying explanations for the scarcity of trained scientist-administrators is found in the confusion of values in the minds of most scientists who have to adjust to our constantly changing, pluralistic society. Polykarp Kusch, an American Nobel Prize laureate, has pointed out that science does not in itself yield value judgments. "It would be dangerous to assume that science alone can produce the bases of decision" he said, "or that it can point to the right course of action as infallibly as it can predict the occurrences of eclipses of the sun. The belief that science can generate the wisdom to solve every problem that faces man is to abdicate his own responsibility in reforming his world."

In a report submitted to Congress by the staff of the House Committee on Science and Astronautics on March 27, 1963, detailing the fifth meeting of the Panel on Science and Technology, Dr. Roger Revelle, the Director of the Scripps Institution of Oceanography, criticized the Chairman for not working the panel harder. He and Dr. Martin Goland, of the Southwest Research Institute, pointed out that the whole set of problems involved more than science and technology, also involving economics, political and social science.

"One of the main lessons that I have learned in the last year and a half here in the Government," Revelle declared, "is the great weakness of most of the Government departments in their ability to analyze these questions that cut across economics, political science, engineering, and technology. In many of the questions, you are faced with a combination of a technical question and an economic or a social question. I think, therefore, that the panels that you have asked to help you should have both kinds of people on them. To begin with, they have just got to learn how to work together before they can perhaps be very useful to you."

Many people falsely assume, Kusch says, that because scientists speak with authority on matters within the scope of science, "it is sometimes thoughtlessly assumed that they also speak with equal authority on almost any subject." In the cases where scientists do speak with great authority on subjects other than science—such as political issues—they usually speak with an authority derived from their experience and knowledge of these other matters, *amplified* by their knowledge of science.

"Public issues to which science is relevant would be much more clearly defined if we [the scientists] are to state with a considerable forcefulness when our statements are within the scope of science and when they are not," Kusch says. "The layman should be taught to distinguish between the pronouncements of a scientist as a scientist and those he makes as an educated man of good will. On matters that are within the technical competence of science, a layman can hardly hope to dispute a scientist; but in other matters the layman may pit his judgments against those of the scientist."

The most dramatic example of a compromise in value judgments by a leading scientific organization was revealed recently—under the glaring Washington spotlight. This first open break between a Federal research fund-granting agency and a scientific fund-receiver occurred in early 1963, when the American Institute of Biological Sciences (AIBS) found its financial accounts under scrutiny by the donor, the National Science Foundation. Until 1960, no drawing accounts at the

NSF were ever examined, and, until recently, American scientists and their organizations receiving Federal funds for various research projects were not policed.

Then an enterprising new NSF comptroller, Aaron Rosenthal, uncovered some discrepancies in the financial accounts of the AIBS. He discovered that some public funds that were earmarked for public research in biology had instead been put into a common pot to pay for the rapidly expanding payroll and overhead of the Institute. Other NSF grants were found being diverted into financing a project which had enriched the coffers of the AIBS. This first public disclosure involving unsupervised Federal scientific NSF research funds to the AIBS broke over the national scene in a cover story by Science Editor John Lear in the March 2, 1963, issue of the *Saturday Review*.

The AIBS had been formed originally in 1948 to present a more effective united front for American biology than the three older splinter biological groups had presented in the past. Since these unity-minded biologists felt their job was to protect the human race from being blown up by their brethren —the bombmakers—they aimed to obtain a voice in the national scientific councils equal to those of the physicists and chemists.

For nine years, the mushrooming AIBS, under the reins of a fireballing executive director, Dr. Hiden Cox (a former botany professor from Virginia Polytechnic Institute), annually fed at the NSF trough. The Institute received Federal handouts to help underwrite its many projects, ranging from a long-range $6 million grant for the revision of high school biology texts and curricula to the purchase of furniture and office equipment for its new headquarters. The NSF issued more contracts to this organization than to any other Federal research grant-seeker. The AIBS also received funds from the Ford Foundation, the AEC, and the Office of Naval Research, as well as the NSF, so that in 1961 the Institute was able to acquire 61 Federal grants totalling $2,240,000 for that year alone.

After noting the unusual growth pattern of the AIBS,

Rosenthal's NSF men by late November, 1962, had come up with a total shortage of some $331,570 in funds that the NSF had granted to the AIBS. The NSF accountants felt that this amount should be "restored" since it had been used for unacceptable "overhead," "travel," and entertainment items. In late February, the NSF reduced its claims against the Institute to $192,000, of which $100,000 was repaid by the AIBS by April 1, 1963. The result of the NSF investigation was a shake-up within the AIBS. Cox was removed as executive director and put in a less sensitive post within the organization, as a "long-range planning officer." Half of the 74 AIBS headquarters employees were dismissed, including five department heads, in the Institute's post-investigation reorganization.

Since the AIBS board members knew and approved of their executive director's method of "commingling" Federal funds with their own into a "general fund," they were as culpable as Cox in the risky business of going "into hock to the NSF." In the aftermath of the image-tarnishing disaster, the members of AIBS were called upon for contributions and increased dues to save the AIBS from bankruptcy and to restore the misspent public funds.

Undoubtedly, one result of the AIBS case will be that the Government will not take the advice of Dr. Dael Wolfe, executive director of the AIBS, who pleaded in an editorial published in the February 8, 1963, issue of *Science* for "new encouragement to the general policy on which most Federal fund granting agencies have worked—that of trusting a grantee [subsidized scientist] instead of constantly policing him." The AIBS audit investigation has opened up a new area of distrust between Government and the scientists that will take many years to repair.

An allied scientific biological controversy occurred during the same period, when Rachel Carson, a noted biological scientist and author, scared the chemical pesticide industry into a state of panic in September, 1962, by the publication of her latest book, *Silent Spring*. The result of four years of intensive research, the book brought about an interesting public relations reaction from scientists who opposed her thesis. In her well-documented classic (which sold over half a million copies in the first eight months after publication) Miss Carson contended: "We have put poisonous and biologically potent chemicals indiscriminately into the hands of persons largely or wholly ignorant of their potentials for harm."

From the "officialese" of some Government science bulletins and pesticide industry releases, observers might conclude that Rachel Carson had advocated a return to the plow. Fortunately, she had such noted scientists as Dr. Frank Egler, who was formerly with the American Museum of Natural History, on her side in the controversy. Egler had long maintained that scientific research into the safety of chemical sprays was under the influence of the chemical industry, which had a direct interest in increased sales of its products. He strongly doubted the objectivity of the many pamphlets printed in rebuttal of *Silent Spring*.

He criticized two recent studies on "Pest Control and Wildlife Relationships," sponsored by the National Academy of Sciences and published in the fall of 1962. "These two bulletins cannot be judged as scientific contributions," Dr. Egler said. "They are written in the style of a trained public relations official of industry, out to placate some segment of the public that is causing trouble." Dr. Ronald Clement, staff biologist of the American Audubon Society, agreed with Egler's denunciation of the NAS studies, thus lowering the prestige of this austere group of scientists.

On April 3, 1963, CBS-TV presented a brilliant hour-long network documentary program on "The Silent Spring of Rachel Carson" which was centered about the controversial book that Supreme Court Justice William O. Douglas called "the most important chronicle for the survival of the human race." After the narrator pointed out that we spend over $800 million each year to bombard insects with 900 million pounds of pesticides which have destroyed more than $14 million in crops, the soft-spoken Miss Carson asked the leading question: "Can anyone believe it is possible to lay down such a barrage of poisons on the surface of the earth without making it unfit for life? They should not be called pesticides but biocides."

She was challenged in her assertion by several leading industrial and Government scientists, foremost of whom was the persuasive Dr. Robert White-Stevens, assistant to the director of American Cyanamid Company and chief spokesman for the chemical industries in their war of words against Miss Carson. He said: "If man were to follow faithfully the teachings of Miss Carson we would return to the dark ages, and insects and diseases and vermin would once again inherit the earth."

Prominent Government scientific officials, like Surgeon General Luther Terry, feel that, in their ability to stamp out diseases like malaria, pesticides have improved human health. Others, like Dr. Arnold Lehman, chief toxicologist of the U.S. Food and Drug Administration, feel that pesticides do not yet exceed the tolerance of safety in the food that we eat. But they may in the future.

Miss Carson pointed out that she was not against all pesticides, but just their indiscriminate use. If we don't control them, they will surely lead us to disaster, she has stated. Her bill of indictment, alerting people to a problem about which they had largely been ignorant, caused Washington to take a new look at the potential hazards of indiscriminate use of pesticides. The great mass of citizenry did not agree with Dr. William Darby of the National Academy of Sciences, who stated bluntly that "this book should be ignored."

Following advance publication of long excerpts from Miss Carson's book in three issues of the *New Yorker* magazine in the summer of 1962, a Government panel was appointed in August to investigate the pesticides. Several key Government scientists testified that we needed controls over the air-borne dusting and spraying with pesticides which sometimes missed their target, destroying harmless wildlife and fish. Dr. John Buckley, director of the U.S. Fish and Wildlife Center, said:

"There is no doubt that the use of pesticides caused losses of 80 per cent or more in our fish and wildlife where they were used in excess." This statement substantiated Miss Carson's charge of needless killing.

Dr. James Hartshering of the President's Committee on Biology of the FCST admitted on the CBS-TV program that we "do not know how long pesticides stay in the soil or their effects." Water pollution expert Dr. Page Nicholson of the U.S. Public Health Service said: "We know very little now, so we need more research." He was seconded by Dr. Buckley who wanted to know more about the rate of concentration of residue of pesticides in fish, birds, and animals to determine the effects of the chemical compounds on vital organs. This shocking revelation—by leading Government experts—that we did not have enough knowledge on many of the issues that Miss Carson raised was disquieting to the viewers.

Although her scientific critics in industry and Government accused Miss Carson of "alarmism," most of them admitted the truth of her basic assertions. The Food and Drug Administration found that some pesticides were too toxic for human consumption, while others caused tumors and cancer in some laboratory animals. Rachel Carson feels that the FDA is overburdened and needs more inspectors. As a direct result of her damning evidence, this Government inspection agency increased its sampling of ⅓ of 1 per cent of food shipments in 1962 to 1 per cent in 1963, but Miss Carson feels that this is still not a large enough sample to protect people from possible harm.

Dr. Lehman, a geneticist as well as chief toxicologist of the FDA, disagreed with her contention that more tests are needed, since he believed it would take at least 20 human generations of testing—more than 500 years—to gather any reliable data. But Miss Carson countered that we can obtain the same data on genetic effects of sprays and aerosols in a much shorter period by tests on laboratory animals. Her solution is to explore the use of biological controls as a substitute for chemical pesticides. The prestige of Government scientists involved in this area of chemical pesticides suffered as the result of her exposure—with their frank admissions that we know so very little about the long-range effects of the pesticides.

Unfortunately, the President's special panel set up in August, 1962, still had not made a report some eight months later because of dissension among the Government's scientific agencies as to what controls should be enacted. The scientists' public debate over man *vs.* the balance of nature was highlighted by Miss Carson's closing statement on the TV program. "We talk in terms of conquest of nature," she said, "but we are not mature enough to see ourselves as part of the universe." The big challenge is to prove our mastery and maturity, not of nature, but of ourselves.

On May 15, 1963, the PSAC finally issued a long report on pesticides. The report was damning and disturbing in its confirmation of the views of Rachel Carson and conservationists that some pesticide chemicals, when improperly used, have killed large numbers of animals, fowl, and fish and have upset the ecological balance of nature. Dr. Wiesner pointed out that, although no one was suggesting that the use of pesticides be halted, man's uncontrolled use of them is potentially a greater hazard than radioactive fallout.

Because the full effects of chemical pollution, in the food we eat and through inhalation and skin absorption, were not yet known, the PSAC urged strong and prompt action to assure the more judicious use of pesticides and called for stronger Federal laws to control the marketing and use of the chemicals. The President, acting immediately, stated that he had already requested responsible Government agencies to implement the recommendations of the report—including the drafting of the legislative proposals. This report was a vindication of scientists, like Miss Carson, who in recent years had warned against the dangers arising from unchecked proliferation of synthetic chemicals and the need for stiffer and better coordinated public controls of these pesticides.

One national group of scientists had become vaguely aware of these public relations problems in recent years. In 1960, the American Association for the Advancement of Science appointed a Committee on Science in the Promotion of Human Welfare. The chairman was Barry Commoner of the University of Washington, and included on the committee were such eminent scientists as Robert Brode of the University of California, Harrison Brown of the California Institute of Technology, and Margaret Mead of the American Museum of Natural History.

This group became concerned with the widening gap between "hard" science and the social sciences. They were also worried about the need for scientists to accept their responsibilities in helping to bridge this gulf and thus "help mediate the effects of scientific progress on human welfare." They questioned the continuation of "the conscious exploitation of science for military advantage . . . at an accelerating rate," and the use in recent years of science as a prestige symbol in international politics.

Realizing that increased Government support for scientific research was motivated to a large degree by the philosophy of trying to "get ahead of the Russians," the committee deplored the concurrent sacrifices to basic research as more and more funds were poured into applied research.

Because of the public misconceptions about the recent developments in science, and the conflict with the conditions of its service to military and political affairs, the committee felt that an unfortunate "nationalistic" cloak was being draped around science. The committee warned the nation that "any effort to divide science into fragments that are delimited by national boundaries . . . will inevitably restrict the free discovery and communication of new knowledge that is the substance of scientific progress. A 'nationalistic' science is an anachronism which cannot long continue without damage to science and eventually to the nation."

Granting that "science serves the nation by serving humanity," the AAAS committee report, made on July 9, 1960, warned that the integrity of science was beginning to erode under the "abrasive pressure of its close partnership with economic, social and political affairs." The report went on: "Recent controversies about the detection of nuclear explosions and fallout problems had seen scientist lined up against fellow scientist—each claiming to be an infallible expert for his point of view. This political approach to the problems only tended to cloud the public mind and reduce the former 'objectivity' of science."

The committee then proceeded to break down the issues into two classes as far as seeking solutions was concerned. The first area concerned the effects of public policy on science itself. In the solutions of these problems, the committee felt that the opinions of the scientists should carry special weight and that scientists should accept the obligation to develop and explain these opinions.

The other area concerned the more difficult social and political problems that did not exclusively involve scientists but which concerned all citizens and had a broad relation to public policy. Examples of this area would be the evolving public policy of the uses and controls of nuclear energy, and the value of insecticides. In this sensitive area, not only are the citizens often in the dark about the roots of the issues, but many scientists, perplexed by the complexities of technical problems, are unable to properly visualize alternative courses of action.

This deficiency on the part of scientists to become aware of their own brainchildren "is a major cause of the difficulties that now impede the proper development of public policy on science related issues," according to the AAAS report.

Since the scientist as an informed citizen in a democratic society is free to express his opinions regarding alternative solutions on matters of public policy, he has the option of joining with like-minded citizens in a group effort to foster the solution that he prefers, according to the scientists who wrote the AAAS Human Welfare Report. But the authors went beyond this step with the bold assertion that "in the matter of providing citizens with the knowledge required to make informed decisions on science related issues, the scientist and his organizations have both a unique competence and a special responsibility. As the producer and custodian of scientific knowledge, the scientific community has the obligation to impart such knowledge to the public."

They should also detect budding problems before they become acute, such as the relationship of nutrition with the development of cancer or the prevention of smog in our cities, the report continued. There still appears to be a lack of agreement, however, on the rule for justifying science's entering the social process as an agency of information. Should scientists restrict themselves to being advisers to the Government on technical matters by invitation only? Because the tenor of the advice is usually conditioned by the peculiar interests of the requesting agency, which restricts the questions asked of the scientific advisers, many dissenters to this limitation feel this function does not therefore fulfill the scientists' social role. In dealing with explosive social issues, the scientific community is thus challenged to demonstrate its responsibility in regard to truth and objectivity on the matter at stake.

The AAAS committee felt that in such cases the scientific community "ought to assume on its own initiative, an independent and active informative role, whether or not other social agencies see any immediate advantage in hearing what the scientist has to say." A citizenry which is thus informed is the chief assurance that science will be devoted to the promotion of human welfare.

In order to improve their channels of information to the public, scientists must find ways to make better use of the communications media. The atomic scientists had realized in 1945—after four years of silence imposed by wartime security—that they were bursting with the need to tell the world about the terrible and wonderful thing that they had wrought.

They felt that the press could play its part in the dissemination of this information. Newspapers and magazines began to treat science news and interviews with such celebrities as Teller and Oppenheimer as newsworthy materials.

In turn, through the communications media, the scientists helped create a demand for the international control of atomic weapons and the termination of the seven-year abomination of the McCarthy purges. But, as Alfred Friendly, managing editor of the Washington *Post,* has pointed out: "They were not all wise, as world government was not notably advanced by some of the luminaries of the sciences . . . and the recruits did not demonstrate that they were the shrewdest practical politicians or opinion leaders who ever came down the pike.

"The scientists and the press should realize," Friendly concluded, "that neither alone nor together, do they have all the answers to the remedies for the world's grief."

The scientists also have to learn to widen and improve communications of their new-found knowledge beyond press interviews. It is not enough for a science professor or Government official to know his subject. He must also learn the knack of communicating this knowledge to Congress, the President, and the public. This means that our scientists have to become better acquainted with the TV medium and its potential. Only Edward Teller seems to have properly mastered the knack of using television to communicate his ideas to the unseen viewing audience.

Scientists also must learn to speak in idioms that the scientifically untrained layman can understand. This means scientists must eliminate most of their technical jargon, and substitute for "missilese" simple terms that are easily translatable to the public. The scientists will have to learn to write better and to express themselves in more vivid popular style without the help of editorial brokers, like those supplied by the excellent staff of the *Scientific American.* Most of them are going to have to learn by themselves to make this transition from the academically dull, turgid prose of their professional journals to the more journalistic language of a Rickover.

Some scientists are of the opinion that their role on policy issues should be restricted to first informing the public about the relevant facts, then explaining the limits of accuracy and the alternate interpretations that apply. Once they have fulfilled their educational function, these men feel that they can then withdraw and let the citizen make his own choice of the possible solutions.

This approach was the basis for the establishment a few years ago of the St. Louis Citizen's Committee for Nuclear Information. This joint group of scientists and citizens was devoted to the dissemination of information about the radiation problem. A similar group of experts, called the Scientist's Committee for Radiation Information, was formed at the same time in New York. Another group of professional scientists, differing slightly from the others, is the Society for Social Responsibility in Science. This group holds that scientists have a moral responsibility to try to limit their applications of science and technology to ethical uses.

The faith of the American public in the high prestige of scientific judgment was somewhat shaken in the spring of 1963 with the growing clamor of dissent over our manned lunar landing program. When Dr. Philip Abelson, in the April, 1963, issue of *Science,* urged that higher priority be given to the exploration of the moon by electronic robots instead of by men, it created a storm of protest within high scientific circles. Abelson, the editor of the AAAS journal, also criticized the postponement of scientific lunar studies in order to speed up the *Apollo* manned landings.

To counter his and other criticisms of the size, cost, and urgency of our manned lunar effort, a group of eight top scientists, including three Nobel laureates, spoke out on May 26, 1963, in support of the American moon program. The signers of the statement, among whom were Nobelists Dr. Joshua Lederberg, chairman of the department of genetics at Stanford University, Dr. Harold Urey, professor of chemistry at California University, and Dr. Willard Libby, director of the Institute of Geophysics and Planetary Physics at California

University, pointed out that "this criticism raises important issues regarding the motives which underlie the United States space effort."

They asked if the "overwhelming" support for the President's plan for a manned lunar landing was "tendered for scientific reasons primarily or was it motivated by a broader concern with national interests and national goals?" They expressed the view that the public and Congress saw in the project "an important contribution to the future welfare and security of the United States. They thus went on record that the moon-landing projects could *not* be done entirely with instruments or be assessed on its scientific merits alone.

There are many other areas where the scientists can expand their activities not only to enhance their prestige but to better the lot of the peoples of the world. They can stress the peaceful types of international activities for the betterment of health, agriculture, and basic research, all over the world. They can encourage more cooperative, IGY type of programs on the land, in the depths of the ocean, and in the far reaches of space. They can foster more international conferences—both Government- and privately sponsored—on peaceful uses of space and atomic energy. They can push for a strong science advisory section in the U.N. similar to that in our own Government and in NATO. Finally, they can support and encourage a revolutionary expansion of education, both on the national and international level, and the establishment of strategically located world science centers.

If these programs could be conducted on a comprehensive basis instead of piecemeal as they are at present, the prestige of scientists would increase proportionately.

# Chapter 19

# What Role Should the Scientists Play in Our Struggle for Survival?

Science can become useless and dangerous to the social order if the basis of scientific integrity becomes compromised. Nowhere was this question of integrity more acute than over the moral issue of where the scientists stood on the question of human survival on the planet. For the basic failure of the nuclear scientists and engineers in particular, in their short history of power and influence during the cold war, has not been their lack of knowledge about the turbulent portents of the future. Rather, their failure can be traced to their acting too frequently as if they *had* knowledge when they *didn't*. This lack of prescience in politics has hurt the prestige of the physical and space scientists more than any other single factor in recent years.

On the twentieth birthday of the atomic age, Dr. Eugene Wigner, who was with Fermi at Chicago back in December, 1942, admitted that at that time he and his fellow scientists made two regrettably inaccurate predictions concerning the future uses of atomic fission. The first prediction was economic, and the second political. The scientists' early economic expectations concerning cheap nuclear power failed to materialize. Technological improvements lowered the operating costs of coal and oil as cheap power fuels and served as an obstacle to the development of the anticipated atomic power plants around the world.

On the second, political expectation, the nuclear scientists were dismayed to discover that far from promoting world security, atomic weapons led instead to the current "balance of terror." This state of affairs, Wigner said, has led many of us today to come nearly full circle in believing that only the abolition of such weapons can avert war and that nuclear disarmament *will,* in fact, have this effect.

"What was the blind spot in our vision?" he asked. "How could we have been so wrong? As scientists, and therefore eager to enshrine reason, we made the false assumption that, with the survival of humanity at stake, nations would set their goals accordingly; that the very existence of nuclear weapons would neutralize potential conflicts and insure world peace. Any other outcome would be utterly irrational.

"What we failed to take into account is the rather obvious fact that conflicts do not arise *logically* but *emotionally;* that they are caused by incompatible ambitions and desires, whether between nations or within a single country. The role of reason is real enough, but it does not determine our goals; it merely teaches us how to attain these, and at what cost.

"In other words, the existence of nuclear weapons may shape a nation's strategy without resolving incompatibilities in its ambitions and desires or fundamentally altering its goals vis-à-vis other nations. A lion is still a lion, no matter how high-powered the rifle that prevents it from attacking the lamb." Here was one scientist who had finally recognized that the scientific method can't solve all our problems. The scientists, like Wigner, have got to take a broader look at the moral problems facing man.

They must ask themselves: is it morally wrong for scientists to work on weapons of mass destruction that might some day boomerang to kill the very hands that created them? Sir Charles P. Snow has pointed out one subtle difference between the morality of soldiers and the morality of scientists. Whereas soldiers must obey orders to kill as the foundation of their morality, a scientist has the fundamental right to "question and rebel." He knows that blind loyalty in itself can turn into a deadly conformity and become a cloak for the timid.

It will take boldness to question the order of things in our complex society, but Snow feels that knowledge itself will eventually become the springboard for moral action on the part of those scientists who wish to help shape our actions in a more positive direction. "Knowledge gives us guts," he says, and "perhaps it can give us guts strong enough for the jobs in hand."

Our scientists have been challenged to reverse the present acceleration toward a thermonuclear holocaust and to make *moral* choices based on the fruit of their inquiries.

Unfortunately, Snow has failed to suggest that the scientist exercise the courage to take the *last* important step of speaking out and saying *what* he knows. He claims he is no anarchist, but just what does a scientist *do* when the Government has reached a decision that goes against his moral fiber? *When* and *how* does he shout "No!"? Does he do it alone and take the chance of going to jail or being laughed at as a nonconforming heretic? Or does he organize a "resistance movement" to thwart the nation's stated purpose? How is the Western scientist who disagrees with his Government to communicate with his fellow Russian and Chinese scientists on the other side of the iron and bamboo curtains?

Which scientist made the *right* moral decision a decade ago? Teller, with his go-ahead to build the H-bomb, or Oppenheimer, with his negative vote? Which set of values carried the most weight for man in the long-range perspective? Teller won the short skirmish; the H-bomb was built and was an explosive success. But, in the long perspective, was not Oppenheimer's cautionary "No" the more humanitarian choice? Possession of the basic know-how helped determine our eventual decision to construct the H-bomb, but wasn't the final decision a political one based on what the policy makers believed would be in the national interest? Knowledge didn't dictate the final American decision on the issue, but it helped indirectly to educate and sway our leaders toward the ultimate decision. In the two-way democratic process, the political leader must educate and persuade the scientists as to what is good for the country and the world.

This political education is necessary to prevent a recurrence of the famous *faux pas* made in 1956 by C. W. Sherwin, then chief scientist for the Air Force, who decided all "social-political devices, such as disarmament and federal world government" were impractical ways to achieve the preservation of peace. He felt that new *scientific* knowledge *alone* offered "a previously unknown technical tool for the assault on the problem of preserving peace." Fortunately, since then other leading scientists have matured and broadened their understanding of the world about them as attested by the following incident which occurred just four years later.

The Committee on Science in the Promotion of Human Welfare of the AAAS was not content to let their case rest with their 1960 pronouncement on the best ways to put science to use in the national interest. A year and a half later, at the Association's year-end meeting in Denver, committee members issued a new paper proposing that scientists evolve a new discipline—"the science of human survival"—which would develop alternatives to the unlimited war which science had now made possible.

This group was concerned with whether we could afford to take the appalling risk of attempting to learn from experience whether humanity could survive a nuclear catastrophe. The committee members asserted that science could not predict that human societies could ever return to their present state of competence following a nuclear war. They warned that even if some unforeseen development should arise to help us survive a nuclear war, we might then be faced with the equally devastating possibilities of a chemical or biological war.

Recognizing that mankind must go on living in a world where suicidal war is a constant possibility, they stated that their "problem is not the prevention of a particular war but the continuous protection of human society from a potential danger that will continue to threaten the human species with extinction.

"Peace, which was until now a human WANT, has become a human NEED," they wrote. "But so long as there is no alternative to war as a means of national security, the need for peace—and for survival—will conflict with the need for social protection." They believe that scientists have a historic opportunity to find an alternative to war.

In order to accomplish their public educational tasks, the scientists will have to overcome certain difficulties, such as the removal of the obstacles that tend to obstruct the flow of technical information to the scientific community, the committee's report continued. Much of the information about war is not easily accessible to scientists.

Another difficulty is the social pressure brought to bear against the scientist who attempts to disseminate any scientific findings about war and peace which support one political belief while contradicting another. In such cases, the panel felt that, in return for the scientists' informing the citizens about the grave issues, their fellow "citizens will have a reciprocal duty to defend the scientists' right to be heard without prejudice."

In serving the social need for peace, scientists must find a means of protecting society that does not run the risk of destroying it. This means that scientists have got to grapple with problems of limitation of armaments, arms inspection, alternatives to war, and the development of new instruments for the maintenance of peace.

Because the complexity of a nuclear test ban treaty obviously involves a wide array of questions in the natural sciences, sociology, and economics, scientists were urgently requested to study new approaches to the problems and to marshal all the sciences to support the ban before it was too late.

The committee then called for a radical combining of the concepts and methods of the physical, biological, and social sciences, which have been separated in the past by their reliance on different approaches. The panel pointed to the success of the interdisciplinary cooperation of the various sciences in IGY, in various U.N. programs, and in the Antarctic. As for dealing with the problem of modern war, science is in a unique position to lead the way because of its adherence to certain established rules of procedure.

Because of science's insistence on the objective, open discussion of results, and continuous correction of its errors and omissions, the report stated, it has taught its practitioners to rely on what we know about nature, rather than on what we *wish* nature to be. Thus, science has a powerful means of correcting faulty human conceptions—such as the belief that human societies can be conserved by modern war.

The AAAS Human Welfare Committee concluded the report by calling for the establishment of a new "collaborative science, *the science of human survival,* which would then apply the full strength and wisdom of all the sciences to the solution of the crisis created by the obsolescence of war." This report was the first significant one of its type to come from a responsible group of American scientists.

Although the scientists do not yet hold the levers of power for the instruments of annihilation that the scientists themselves have invented, there is still the question of whether an increased possession of political power would make them behave more responsibly or soberly than the politicians who now control these decisions. Our Government, and others too, have found that science accommodates its judgments to fit the current political necessities, as did the Soviet scientists who wailed at our atmospheric testing while remaining silent on their own.

The means of carrying out scientific recommendations had been stymied for the past 19 years by the divisive split within the scientific community. The chief antagonists were two loose groups of physical scientists: the "anti-suicide group" headed by Linus Pauling, Leo Szilard, and Hans Bethe; and the "suicide group" led by Edward Teller.

The outspoken Nobel scientist Linus Pauling, who was attacked by Senator McCarthy in 1950 as "having a well nigh incredible record of membership in Communist front organizations," was harassed on several occasions in 1959 and 1960 by the Senate Internal Security Subcommittee. Under the chairmanship of Democratic Senator Thomas Dodd of Connecticut, this committee called the Cal Tech chemist to Capitol Hill to explain the nuclear test-ban petition which he circulated in 1957. This manifesto was signed by 11,021 scientists in 49 countries and was subsequently presented to the United Nations on January 15, 1958.

In this declaration pleading for an immediate international agreement to stop all testing of nuclear weapons, Pauling and the other scientists urged that this move "could serve as a first step towards a more general disarmament, and the effective abolition of nuclear weapons." Their dramatic U.N. petition led to the re-emergence of the "control school" group of scientists, who had been in a state of lethargy ever since the green light was given to develop the hydrogen superbomb.

Knowing full well that his testimony could lead to a jail term and a contempt of Congress citation, Pauling appeared before Congress and explained his position in an easy, eloquent manner. He agreed to give the committee the names of the people to whom he wrote and the names on the petition, but, when he was asked for the names of the people who helped collect the signatures, he refused because he knew from experience that giving names to Congressional committees led only to reprisals. He believed that these people had only exercised their constitutional right to petition the Government.

Up until this point, the hearings were genteel, but then Pauling was confronted with a demand to return before the subcommittee with the names. A delay was granted, and when he came back to testify again on October 11th, the demand was not pushed.

In recent years, Pauling has resigned his administrative posts as head of the Chemical Engineering Department at Cal Tech and has devoted himself to the fight against nuclear weapons. His book *No More War,* published in 1958, was an eloquent plea to stop nuclear testing because of the genetic hazards. He has attended most of the Pugwash Conferences and has spoken before the Japanese Diet against atomic and hydrogen bombs. Pauling tends to oversimplify the issues and talk about problems of war and peace in terms of absolutes. To this day, he sees no justification for Hiroshima and Nagasaki. Many colleagues feel that he has lost his effectiveness as a crusader by taking a utopian position, but he is still admired for his independence and fighting courage.

Hans Bethe, the other scientific peace leader of comparable stature, told the Senate in 1959 that "the most important point in achieving a test suspension is a *political* one; namely, to obtain a controlled disarmament agreement. And if we once get one . . . I believe that others may follow, and that the principle will thereby be established." He felt that this move would halt the arms race.

Unfortunately, our failure to achieve a test ban by mid-1963 can be traced to our avoidance of any attempt to intertwine the technical and political aspects of the problem. The strict separation that was maintained on our side of the fence between the technical and political realms—with no panel of political and scientific experts examining the issues—further hurt our efforts. So our policy continued to be a vacillating one, particularly at the Geneva Conference of Experts, where we were to learn a bitter lesson.

Bethe and Pauling's chief antagonist was the fiery Edward Teller—the father of the H-bomb. Strangely enough, he was the first noted scientist to warn the public about the dangers of fallout in an article in the *Bulletin of the Atomic Scientists* in February, 1947. His predictions came true seven years later, when the small Japanese fishing trawler, *The Lucky Dragon,* was unluckily subjected to ashy radioactive rain 100 miles from a bomb test site. From 1954 on, the subject of fallout was no longer academic. It was real.

The bitterness of the conflict over fallout between the two major opposing schools of thought was unparalleled in the previous history of scientific controversy over nuclear weapons policy. Pauling, the protagonist on one side, interpreted the evidence to show that fallout was equivalent to the plague, while Teller, who championed the other side, actually led his followers to believe that fallout could even be beneficial.

On December 1, 1961, 61-year-old Dr. Leo Szilard, who was professor of biophysics at the Enrico Fermi Institute for Nuclear Studies at the University of Chicago and the holder of the patent on the control process for the first nuclear chain reaction, proposed that scholars and scientists organize a lobby for peace. Having escaped death from cancer earlier that year, Szilard decided to spend his remaining years expanding the nucleus of his lobby into a "nationwide movement for abolishing war."

He got the idea after lecturing on the subject to enthusiastic audiences at several university campuses throughout the country. He told the students of his discouragement after spending a year in the nation's capital trying to convince Government officials of the hazards of a nuclear arms build-up. "There is no market for wisdom in Washington," he said. "Government officials are too concerned with day-to-day crises. There are too many pressures." He concluded that the problem of disarmament was mainly a "political" one, and that as long as our Government was not serious about the problem no one else would be. He believed that only those scholars and scientists who "have sufficient passion for the truth to give the truth a chance to prevail should be brought to Washington" in his lobby. Although he admitted that a few U.S. Senators possessed insight into the world situation and were concerned about it, he said that "mostly they lack the courage of their convictions."

Szilard, a brilliant scientist but a naïve politician, hoped to help the citizenry realize that the production of more nuclear weapons could lead us only to a dead-end street and disaster for all. Therefore, he sought steps to try to reverse the arms race by prevailing upon our leaders to give up our weapons stockpile before a dozen other nations got nuclear weapons. President Kennedy, in his press conference of March 21, 1963, predicted this would happen by 1970 to 1975.

Szilard proposed that his peace lobby work for a seven-point program of "political objectives" designed to end our "first strike" policy. This policy was based on the ability to strike Russia and China with such force that they would not be able to strike back in a nuclear war. It could lead only to a "sky-is-the-limit" arms race, he believed. He proposed instead an invulnerable second strike force that could return a nuclear attack no matter how powerful. He felt that this idea could open the door to an arms control agreement.

As a first step to a final agreement, Szilard proposed two unilateral agreements with Russia and China: first, that we would not bomb enemy cities and bases unless we or our allies were attacked; second, that in a war we would use atomic weapons for defense only. He hoped within the year to enlist 500,000 people into an intellectual pressure group, each member of which would be willing to contribute 2 per cent of his income to support the lobbyists and staff in Washington. He felt there was a strong need for such a great popular contribution toward achieving world peace in the ten short years that he believed was all the time that we had left. He was confident that if he could get just a few Congressmen interested, his appeal would be successful.

By April, 1962, when his common-sense speech, "Are We on the Road to War?" was reprinted in the *Bulletin of the Atomic Scientists,* Szilard had already given his challenging lecture at nine American colleges and universities in order to invite the students as well as the faculty to participate in the experiment. Many in his college audiences responded, as did 2,500 of the 30,000 subscribers to the *BAS.*

On June 2, 1962, the Council for Abolishing War was officially established in Washington as "an organization of desperation," and announcements were sent out to all those who had pledged their support. Prior to the establishment of the

CAW, the Scientists Committee for a Livable World had been formed to work for disarmament. Szilard invited their officers to Washington and used this group as a nucleus of his new peace organization. More than $55,000 was contributed during the course of the summer for the operating expenses of the Council.

Actually, the CAW was an attempt to put into action the *BAS* editorial policies, and to create, beyond the readers of the journal, a mass movement that would support politicians in Washington who would push for disarmament.

In the fall of 1962, a decision was made to concentrate on the election campaigns of three "peace-minded" Senators: George McGovern of South Dakota, Joseph Clark of Pennsylvania, and Wayne Morse of Oregon. The sum of $50,000 was split among the three candidates—with half going to support McGovern and Clark. Morse, Jacob Javits of New York, and Stuart Hughes, the independent senatorial peace candidate from Massachusetts, split the rest. Significantly, the first four men won their Senate seats, McGovern squeaking home by only a 200-vote margin, so the CAW's contributions for his campaign were crucial to his victory. The Council in its first year had proved that money could be raised to help peace candidates run for office.

Dr. Bernard Feld, president of the Council for Abolishing War and a Szilard protégé, is one of the leading nuclear scientists who have taken the stand that disarmament is the *only* way to stop the spiraling arms race. He recently announced that the Council's aim in 1963–1964 is to raise approximately $10 million for the 1964 national election campaign. With contributions averaging $100 per person, he believes this goal can be achieved with 100,000 members by 1964.

The second aim of the Council's lobbying operation is to educate Congressmen to "spread the word" of peace through a process of self-education. The campaign will be concentrated first in the Senate and then in the House. The CAW hopes to develop a group of a dozen Senators with interest and influence in disarmament legislation and the economic problems that would follow disarmament.

The third program of the Council is devoted to work in the United Nations to reduce arms along the lines of the Soviet plan for general and complete disarmament.

The original group of rather naïve physical scientists organized themselves for effective political action with the aid of several less naïve social scientists. These men have served as advisers to the infant CAW, which is aimed at going beyond the pioneering efforts of the National Committee for a SANE Nuclear Policy.

The Council has hopes of obtaining a cross-membership on the local level with such national peace organizations as Turn Towards Peace and SANE in a cooperative and not competitive program. Dr. Homer Jack, executive director of SANE, however, feels that the scientists' efforts can lead only to a division of the American peace movement in its search for the scanty funds available. Jack believes that the scientists' ego drive in forming the CAW as an independent effort has hurt the peace movement by disrupting the unity that is essential for it to flourish. This feeling was shared by SANE and other peace groups, who felt frustrated and impotent to do anything constructive during the Cuban crisis of 1962.

One lesson which the Council learned in its 1962 political lobbying efforts was that candidates could not run exclusively on a "peace" issue (as Hughes did in Massachusetts) without inviting political suicide. In the future they are going to concentrate on electing "good" candidates, who are interested in peace. On the more positive side, the leaders of the CAW's inner sanctum got to talk with McGeorge Bundy, Secretary of Defense McNamara, and Dr. Wiesner on the issue of disarmament, something that no other American peace group had been able to do before. The Council feels that we need Congressional legislation to make conversion from cold war to peacetime production profitable. At present CAW has only a vague idea about the development of institutions for a world law that will arise if nuclear disarmament becomes a reality. Dr. Feld has admitted that the Council made an initial mistake by limiting its early efforts to college campuses and readers of the *BAS*. For this reason, the average man in the street still does not know about the Council's aims and activities. It has not yet approached any leading defense industries, such as General Dynamics (as the Arms Control and Disarmament Agency has done) to persuade the management to influence their employees to work for the establishment of economic construction after disarmament comes.

The Council has remained above the seven-year struggle between the Geneva diplomats who are trying to hammer out a nuclear test ban agreement. These prolonged talks are the key for achieving progress toward complete disarmament.

In the attempt to reach a test ban agreement in Geneva, our Conference of [State Department and AEC] Experts made an important switch during the twenty-sixth meeting on August 5, 1958. Theretofore, the diplomatic responsibility of our delegation had been narrowly prescribed to reach a technical agreement with the Eastern delegations on a limited spectrum of control systems. After that meeting, however, our delegates changed their tactics and began to bargain with the Communist negotiators, trying to commit the latter to a control system similar to that drawn up by the American panel of nuclear experts under Hans Bethe.

But the Russians had already made their switch (though they somewhat disguised it), during the eighteenth meeting on July 23rd. In their maneuver for political advantage during the "technical" talks held on that day, the scientific head of the Russian delegation suggested to Dr. James Fisk of the American group that the text of the agreement be modified to restrict flights of aircraft for meteorological purposes and collecting radioactive samples to over *ocean* areas instead of over *small seas*.

Fisk, in the interest of saving words, agreed to replace *small seas* by *oceans*. Semyon Tsarapkin, sitting at Federov's elbow, added, "Over the oceans-*plural!*" He wanted to make clear that all five oceans would be included. Once again, Fisk agreed to accept the change. The American delegate had fallen into a Soviet trap. He should have inquired about the legal difference between *high seas* and *oceans*. The change in the legal meaning of the agreement signified that no radioactive sampling aircraft inspection flights could be possible near the Soviet Union, since the U.S.S.R. is bounded solely by "seas," except for the lower extremity of the Kamchatka peninsula. This regrettable error was caused by our delegate's failure to be coached in the finer points of international law . . . and geography.

Even Fisk later realized that technical and political arguments cannot be separated for long and that the Soviets had recognized the interplay between these two forces from the beginning. Their chief delegate Semyon Tsarapkin, a shaggy haired little man with an unprepossessing manner (who was nicknamed "Old Scratchy" by the American delegation), was one of their toughest negotiators. The wily Tsarapkin, who set up the strategy to get us to change the text from *seas* to *oceans,* emerged in a few months as the head of the Soviet "political" delegation on the test ban treaty. So, in the follow-up "political" talks, he had only to maintain the position he and his colleagues had already established in the "technical" talks.

In September of 1961, both sides had agreed upon the McCloy–Zorin principles of general disarmament stages with a balanced amount of inspection. The only failures have been in agreement on the details and procedures of inspection, and the timing and phasing of arms reduction.

The Soviet disarmament plan envisions a rapid elimination of delivery systems in the first stage—consisting of rockets, planes, and submarines—with inspection only over the destruction of weapons and no internal inspection until the final stages.

The American plan proposed a gradual, 30 per cent elimination of vehicles over the first three years, reaching a 50 per cent figure by the end of the second stage, with inspection.

The basic difficulty in arriving at a first-step agreement has been the distrust shown by the U.S., since we enjoyed a superiority in weapons over the U.S.S.R. As long as we have this superiority, we could eliminate *all* Soviet bases in a "first strike" situation. We have not yet ruled out this idea from our "preventive" war plans, should the Soviets ever become brash enough to attempt to overrun Western Europe with conventional weapons.

The first major break in the Geneva diplomatic disarmament deadlock occurred in late 1962, when the West agreed to a policy that a meaningful first stage of disarmament would have to be large but not complete. After blasting the U.S. on its Cuban policy, Valerian Zorin told the U.N. General Assembly at the end of his speech that the U.S.S.R. was revising its plan for a "black box" approach to inspection. The U.S. had something to trade in this compromise proposal, i.e., backing the Western concession of progressive zonal inspection, which would guarantee to the U.S.S.R. that large parts of its territory would be free from inspection in the early stages. This was an important step.

On August 27, 1962, the U.S. and Britain had presented a reasonable new draft treaty to the eighteen-nation Disarmament Conference in Geneva. This treaty contained a proposal to end nuclear testing in all environments and an alternative treaty to end testing in the atmosphere, space, and underwater only.

During the long-drawn-out negotiations to achieve a workable nuclear test ban treaty, neutral Sweden finally came up with a compromise solution to end an impasse between the U.S. and the U.S.S.R. On November 28, 1962, Rolf Edberg, head of the Swedish delegation, proposed an interim commission of international scientists to prepare a permanent treaty. While this is being worked out, he suggested a moratorium with a time limit to be agreed upon by the three nuclear powers, the U.S., U.S.S.R., and Britain. Edberg said that his proposed interim commission must be furnished with modern electronic equipment and quick communications. He told the conference he was eager to emphasize the "purely scientific and nonpolitical character" of the proposed international monitoring machinery. "We must count upon science, working and analyzing objectively, as our foremost ally," he said. "If we do not act soon, it will be too late because we do not know how long the favorable circumstances, which now seem to facilitate an agreement, will last."

Afterward, Arthur Dean, head of the U.S. delegation, unfortunately disparaged the proposal by asking who was to "pay for the unorganized professors." His off-the-cuff remarks did not get a friendly reception from the Swedish and other neutral delegates. Later, another American delegate tried to smooth the ruffled feathers of the most protocol conscious of the neutralist nations by stating that the Swedish proposal would be "studied carefully."

By contrast, Semyon K. Tsarapkin, the scientist-diplomat who headed the Soviet delegation, immediately said that the Swedish proposal would be "scrutinized with the utmost care." Privately, he told diplomats that the Soviet Union would view the proposal favorably *if* it accepted the Russian idea of "invitational" inspection of suspicious underground explosions. The Soviet delegate underlined the immobility of his country's position when he commented that the U.S. and Britain "obviously" did not intend to cease underground tests since "everybody knows" that they were preparing new tests in Nevada.

One of the major reasons for the test ban impasse at Geneva has been the extraordinary effectiveness of Dr. Teller and his group, who have mobilized opinion against test cessation. Their position has not always been completely consistent, particularly when Teller argued for underground testing after President Eisenhower initiated a ban on atmospheric testing because of the fallout danger. Teller said that fallout was not a factor then, but, when underground testing began, he argued that atmospheric testing was also essential. During the beginning of the test ban negotiations at Geneva, Teller argued against any treaty that did not provide for on-site inspection. When the Soviets finally accepted this principle, which was welcomed by President

Kennedy, Teller argued against any test ban, *with* or *without* inspection.

In late January, 1963, the Republican National Conference Committee on Nuclear Testing asked various "experts" on the subject to submit papers to them. Not surprisingly, the first papers published were authored by Dr. Edward Teller and Admiral Lewis Strauss and opposed a treaty in any form. Most of the other "experts" also followed this line, opposing anything less than a "rascal-proof" treaty.

In the House, Representative Craig Hosmer, a Republican from California, attempted to turn the nuclear test ban talks at Geneva into a partisan political issue. He established a G.O.P. panel to seek "scientific advice" on an inspection system. The character of the advice sought and received by the G.O.P. by February, 1963, was indicated by the fact that *all* its statements released at the time of the panel's first report were *hostile* to a nuclear test agreement—with the *sole* exception of a mild statement by Director William Foster of the U.S. Arms Control and Disarmament Agency.

Although Teller has been called "emotional" by his critics, some of his scientist detractors have unfortunately resorted to the same type of sensationalism in their attacks upon his views. Eight prominent scientists, including Phillip Morrison and Bernard Feld, assailed him with such words as "madness," "self-deception," "arrogant nonsense," "preposterous," and an "escape into an insane world" in their article "An Answer to Teller," in the April 14, 1962, *Saturday Evening Post.*

In mid-March, 1963, as the result of some new scientific detection advances, America offered a concession to the Russians, by substantially reducing the area that each on-site inspection would cover. This policed area would cover underground nuclear tests. The Russian delegate, Tsarapkin, promptly brushed the plan aside, calling it an attempt to "sabotage the discussion of a test ban by bringing in technical matters. By getting into technicalities," he said, "we may talk for another ten years."

Charles C. Stelle, U.S. Ambassador to the Geneva test ban

conference, disclosed that the first detailed Western plan for our reduced inspection procedures provided that any on-site inspection would cover a maximum of 500 square kilometers (equal to 193 square miles). The U.S. had previously demanded an inspection area of 700 to 800 kilometers to determine whether suspicious underground disturbances were earthquakes or banned nuclear explosions.

The Russians previously had proposed a maximum of three on-site inspections annually and refused to discuss the new U.S. offers until the West accepted their limitation. The West has assumed that at least seven inspections would be needed each year on the territory of each of the nuclear powers. The multinational inspection teams would include 14 members, according to the American plan.

Meanwhile, back in Washington the Senators who were opposed to any test ban treaty were accusing the administration of making too many concessions to the Soviets. Senator Thomas Dodd listed 12 separate retreats on our part regarding the numbers and kind of on-site inspections to insure that the Russians did not cheat. Since a two-thirds approval by the Senate was needed on any treaty, Majority Whip Hubert Humphrey pleaded eloquently with his fellow solons, telling them that improved techniques of detection have made it possible to cut down on the number of sites. He said, "We have made no concessions to the Soviet Union; we have made a concession to science; we have made a concession to technology." He was also defending the "truth-telling record" of the administration which had been under fire because of its actions in the Cuban crisis. It was highly doubtful that he made any converts on the Senate floor. He and President Kennedy both were gloomy about hopes for achieving a treaty in the spring of 1963.

President Kennedy added to the pessimism in Washington in a late spring press conference when he predicted that "the genie would be out of the bottle" if we did not get a test ban agreement by the fall—and after then we would never be able to get it back in.

Scientists can help dispel this political gloom. Harrison Brown said in his 1961 Phi Beta Kappa address: "Before disarmament can progress, there must be an agreement, and that agreement must be universal. Before there can be an agreement there must be negotiation and negotiation will take time. In the meantime, what do we do? I fear that we have no choice. We are trapped in the arms race, and until a reasonable agreement is reached aimed at ending it, we must pursue it—attempting the while to avoid rocking the boat unduly, and doing everything we can to introduce stabilizing elements into the system. In doing this, however, we must recognize that at the best it is a stopgap measure—and a distasteful one at that. It is in this area that scientists can play an enormously important role. The task of maintaining military strength and at the same time restraining ourselves from undertaking provocative developments which might trigger military action, is an extraordinarily difficult one."

Those scientists who are seeking some guidance as to what role to play in our dramatic struggle for survival on this planet would do well to turn for advice to the towering figure of the foremost scientist of the twentieth century. It was Albert Einstein who once said: "Until we are taught what our history books do not teach—that the fault is usually ours quite as much as some other nation's, we must have not taken the first step to that wisdom which alone can save us. . . . I believe if the statesmen of the world will understand what is at stake they will not ask if it is possible to form a world government. They will realize it is absolutely necessary—or a great part of humanity will be killed without need."

They can turn also to nonscientist President John F. Kennedy who challenged the nation and the world in his Inaugural Address: "Let us invoke the wonders of science instead of its terrors. Let us expand our effort to explore the stars, to conquer the deserts, to eradicate disease, to tap the ocean depths, to increase commerce."

The limited nuclear test ban treaty which was finally agreed upon in Moscow by Foreign Minister Andrei Gromyko of the U.S.S.R., Viscount Hailsham, British Minister of Science, and W. Averell Harriman, U.S. Undersecretary of State for Political Affairs, on July 25, 1963, was literally forced upon three of the four leading nuclear powers by the scientists of the world. The continuous expression of their fears, based on the possibility that dangerous genetic effects would plague future generations of the world if the underwater, atmospheric, and space atomic tests were indefinitely prolonged, finally motivated the political leaders to taking action.

The end of above-ground testing by the signatories terminated their contribution to the radioactive contamination of our planet's environment, of the air we breathe, of the food we eat, and of the water we drink. The gain to humanity from this agreement, brought about by the insistence of the influential scientists that their nuclear creation must be controlled, not only relieved the peoples of the world of the hazard of nuclear fallout from testing, but marked the first major breakthrough to peace achieved by American and other scientists since the end of World War II. This first small step toward disarmament in 18 years signified a positive hope for the survival of mankind on this planet.

The long parade of witnesses who appeared on Capitol Hill to testify on the nuclear test-ban treaty during late August reached a dramatic pitch when it came to the scientists' turn. Dr. Edward Teller, a strong advocate of intensive atmospheric testing, told the Senate that the "signing was a mistake. If you ratify the treaty, you will have committed an enormously greater mistake." Teller's chief objection was that the U.S. would be unable to perfect an anti-ballistic missile (ABM), a weapon which he contended was well within the present Soviet know-how.

But the "father of the H-bomb" found himself rebutted by a large group of equally prominent scientists headed by Dr. Harold Brown, the Pentagon's research and development chief, Dr. George Kistiakowsky, a former Eisenhower science adviser, and Dr. Herbert York, former head of ARPA in the Eisenhower Administration, who said that Teller was "behind the times." Dr. Norris Bradbury, the head of the Los Alamos Laboratory since 1954, also opposed Teller's views, but Dr. John Foster of the Livermore Lab. partially supported him, feeling that the scientists would get "rusty" if tests were stopped. Although the scientists were split over the issue, the overwhelming majority, including the 16-member PSAC, approved the treaty.

Two other famed atomic scientists, Dr. Leo Szilard and Dr. Hans Bethe, gave strong support for the test-ban treaty in letters to the Foreign Relations Committee. Bethe discounted Teller's qualifications as a witness on the ABM. "The scientists who have looked at the entire ABM problem seem unanimously in the opposite opinion to Dr. Teller, who has only worked on a small phase of this problem—the nuclear weapon," he said.

Teller stood forlorn and alone as the only scientific spokesman who unqualifiedly called for treaty rejection during Senate testimony. Yet he managed to receive more attention from the communications media than all of the pro-treaty scientists combined. Senator Stuart Symington (D., Mo.) demolished Teller without naming him when he observed during the hearings that "Some of the able, experienced and completely honorable scientists who testified against the treaty made mistakes in fact, apparently because in the reasonably recent past they had not been cleared for all classified information. Specifically, apprehensions in the ABM field were not borne out . . . in the highly classified intelligence briefings we received. . . ."

It was a pity that Teller's scientific opposition did not receive equal opportunities to express themselves. For instance, Dr. Seaborg, who supported the treaty, was not even called to testify by any of the Senate committees which conducted hearings on the proposal.

After listening for a week to the parade of pro and con witnesses, California Republican Thomas Kuchel addressed a plaintive appeal to Nobel Prizewinning chemist Dr. Willard Libby:

*Kuchel:* "Let me put my tattered Senatorial toga over your shoulders for a moment. How would you make a decision when some scientists urge that we approve it and others that we disapprove it?"

*Libby:* "Well, Senator, you have no choice but to make up your own mind."

*Kuchel:* "You can give me my toga back."

The Senate Foreign Relations Committee made their decision on August 29th, with a near unanimous 16–1 vote approving the test-ban treaty without reservations. It was finally overwhelmingly passed by a Senate vote of 80–19 on September 24, 1963, after a prolonged debate. The scientists' opinions helped to turn the tide. A victory for peace had been achieved. A new era for mankind—and science—had begun.

The supreme tribute to the scientists' keen role in setting the stage for the nuclear test-ban treaty came on October 10, 1963, with the announcement from Oslo that the Nobel Peace Prize for 1962 (which had not been given for that year) had been awarded to the American scientist, Linus Pauling. This was his second Nobel award—he received his first for chemistry in 1954. His latest prize was given for his leadership against conducting further nuclear tests—an award which he felt "belonged to all scientists who worked for world peace."

# Epilogue

During most of our nation's history, the Federal government regarded science as useful, but not crucial, to our national security and public welfare. Since 1945, the Government and science have joined together in a team effort, with the new triple partnership between Washington on one side and the university and industry on the other already profoundly modifying our former concepts of what is *public* and what is *private* in our national life.

The scientist members of this partnership have been engaged in the political sphere since they breached the traditionally sacred barriers erected between the technical advice and policy-making departments of our Government. Acceptance of this reality means that both sides will now have to learn to live in a more cooperative manner than they have done during the past two decades—when so often they viewed each other with suspicion and distrust. The new forms of institutional pluralism that are evolving from this troika partnership must be kept in balance if our institutions and individual freedom are going to survive the trials of the next decades.

Otherwise, Big Science will most certainly take over our society and become our master. It is not enough to deny that Big Science can control us, because of the broad, random evolution of our culture that is going on at all times, as Dr. Wiesner sincerely believes. One has to take a more positive approach to the problem, otherwise we may wake up one day soon and discover that it actually has gained control over our existence.

Michael Oakeshott in his *Nationalism In Politics,* published in 1963, has penned a memorable passage on our current political dilemma, which should be helpful to our scientists and public: "In political activity, then, men sail a boundless and bottomless sea; there is neither harbor for shelter nor floor for anchorage, neither starting place nor appointed destination. The enterprise is to keep afloat on an even keel; the sea is both friend and enemy; and the seamanship consists in using the resources of a traditional manner of behavior to make a friend of every hostile occasion."

This philosophical guideline written by a prominent lecturer at the London School of Economics could be useful to our rather naïve natural scientists as they plunge deeper into the turbulent waters of politics, to help them fathom its realities, or choose to cross the swaying bridge from the logical, orderly laboratory to the emotion-packed political arena. The scientists will then be in a better position to follow as well as lead. They must learn to not always try to *force* the direction which society should take through the new ocean of space, and in the technologically ordered culture here on earth.

On Lincoln's Birthday, 1963, American scientists received some free advice—from this side of the ocean—on the future direction of their political activities. After nearly a decade had passed since he rendered the historic Supreme Court decision that outlawed segregation in the public schools, Chief Justice Earl Warren journeyed to Atlanta, to speak at a ceremony commemorating the seventy-fifth anniversary of the founding of Georgia Institute of Technology. When he arrived in the Georgia capital, he was greeted by large signs calling for his impeachment. A cordon of police guarded him during his visit.

Before a packed audience of 4,000 students and faculty members, who gave him a standing ovation, Warren paid tribute to our great Constitution as serving our needs today as it did 175 years ago. Then, without mentioning the sensitive issue of civil rights or desegregation, he predicted that the Constitution "will serve as well 175 years in the future if we nurture it as a divine document . . . by bringing coherent legal light to bear upon the ever-changing conditions of life wrought by the wonderful age of science."

The Chief Justice acknowledged that if science is to serve the peaceful purposes of mankind, it "must be given a peaceful setting in both domestic and world law," a factor which he said is so far lacking. The law has not kept pace with science in the onrushing space age, he said. He cautioned that man *can* destroy himself unless the two are made partners for useful outlets.

"A world that is governed by law," he concluded, "will not permit these great discoveries of science to be used for destructive purposes, but a world without law is hell-bent for destruction with or without scientific discoveries." Scientists in politics should take heed of Warren's suggestions, and constructively channel their social talents in the future.

# Selected Bibliography

## I. BOOKS

Alsop, Joseph and Stewart, *We Accuse (The Trial of J. Robert Oppenheimer)*. Simon and Schuster, New York, 1954.

Dupré, Stephen and Lakoff, Sanford, *Science and the Nation: Politics and Policy*. Prentice-Hall, Englewood Cliffs, N.J., 1962.

Gilpin, Robert, *American Scientists and Nuclear Weapons Policy*. Princeton University Press, Princeton, N.J., 1962.

Groves, General Leslie R., *Now It Can Be Told: The Story of the Manhattan Project*. Harper and Row, New York, 1962.

Jungk, Robert, *Brighter than a Thousand Suns, A Personal History of the Atomic Scientists*. Harcourt, Brace and Co., New York, 1958.

Kahn, Herman, *On Themonuclear War*. Princeton University Press, Princeton, N.J., 1960.

Lapp, Ralph, *Kill—and Overkill: The Strategy of Annihilation*. Basic Books, New York, 1962.

Oakeshott, Michael, *Rationalism in Politics*. Basic Books, New York, 1963.

Piel, Gerard, *Science in the Cause of Man*. Alfred Knopf, New York, 1962.

Price, Don K., *Government and Science,* New York University Press, New York, 1954.

Rabinowitch, Eugene (edited by Harlan Cleveland), *The Promise of World Tensions*. The Macmillan Co., New York, 1961.

Snow, C. P., *Two Cultures and the Scientific Revolution*. Cambridge University Press, New York, 1959.

## II. SELECTED ARTICLES AND PAPERS

Anderson, Sen. Clinton P., "Top Secret: But Should It Be?" *New York Times Magazine*. May 3, 1959.

Bok, Enid Curtis, "The Establishment of NASA: The Political Role of the Advisory Scientists," unpublished paper read at the AAAS annual meeting at Philadelphia, Pa. December 27, 1962.

Brode, Wallace, "Development of Science Policy," *Science.* January 1, 1960.

Cousins, Norman, "Experiment at Andover," *The Saturday Review.* November 10, 1962.

Finer, Herman, "Government and the Expert," *Bulletin of the Atomic Scientists.* November, 1960.

Friendly, Alfred, Jr., "Scientists Meet the Press," *Bulletin of the Atomic Scientists.* November, 1956.

Glass, Bentley, "Scientists in Politics," *Bulletin of the Atomic Scientists.* May, 1962.

Hall, Harry, "Scientists and Politicians," *Bulletin of the Atomic Scientists.* February, 1956.

Kusch, Polykarp, "Scientists and the Laymen," *The Key Reporter.* Summer, 1961.

Lang, Daniel, "A Scientist's Advice" (Profile of Dr. Jerome Wiesner), *The New Yorker.* January 19, 1963, Part I; January 26, 1963, Part II.

Lear, John, "Mr. Smithson's Space Station," *The Saturday Review.* May 3, 1958.

Lear, John, "Morality in Science—Report on a Crisis," *The Saturday Review.* March 2, 1963.

Lear, John, "The Facts About the 1962 Space Bomb," *The Saturday Review.* April 6, 1963.

Noyes, W. Albert, "Do We Need a Foreign Policy in Science?" *Bulletin of the Atomic Scientists.* September, 1957.

Rabi, Dr. I. I., "The Cost of Secrecy," *The Atlantic.* August, 1960.

Rabinowitch, Eugene, "To Build or Not to Build?" *Bulletin of the Atomic Scientists.* November, 1961.

Sheehan, Robert, "Thompson, Ramo, Wooldridge: Two Wings in Space," *Fortune.* February, 1963.

Simpson, Mary, "The Scientist in Politics; On Top or on Tap?" *Bulletin of the Atomic Scientists.* January, 1960.

Solo, Robert, "Gearing Military R&D to Economic Growth," *Harvard Business Review.* November–December, 1952.

Sponsler, George, "Needed: Scientists on Top," *Bulletin of the Atomic Scientists.* June, 1962.

Staley, Eugene, "Scientific Development and Foreign Policy," *Science*. January, 1960.

Szilard, Leo, "Are We on the Road to War?" *Bulletin of the Atomic Scientists*. April, 1962.

Waterman, Alan T., "National Science Foundation: A Ten Year Resume," *Science*. May 6, 1960.

Weinberg, Dr. Alvin, "Impact of Large Scale Science in the United States," *Science*. July 21, 1961.

White, Theodore, "Where Do We Fit In, Scientists Ask?" *New York Times Magazine*. May 18, 1958.

Wigner, Eugene, "Twentieth Birthday of the Atomic Age," *New York Times Magazine*. December 2, 1962.

Wolk, Herman, "Science, Politics and the Bomb," *Air Force*. October, 1962.


## III. SPEECHES

Brown, Harrison, "Science and Government," AAAS, Phi Beta Kappa Address, Sigma Xi, Denver, Col. December 29, 1961.

Chase, Edward, "Politics and Technology," *The Yale Review*. Spring, 1963.

Dryden, Hugh, "Toward the New Horizons of Tomorrow," *Astronautics*. January, 1963. First Annual ARS Von Kármán Lecture, Los Angeles, Calif. November, 1962.

Kahn, Herman, "Planning Two Technological Revolutions Ahead," Institute of Aerospace Sciences, New York. January 23, 1962.

Killian, James R., "Science and Public Policy," AAAS, Washington, D.C. December 30, 1958. (Adapted for European presentation, February, 1963.)

Killian, James R., "Making Science a Vital Force in Foreign Policy," Address, M.I.T. Club of New York. December 13, 1960.

Killian, James R., "M.I.T. Centennial Address," Boston. April 18, 1961.

Kistiakowsky, George B., "Science and Foreign Affairs," Fenton Lecture, University of Buffalo. Buffalo, N.Y. October 31, 1960.

Rabi, I. I., "Convocation," University of Rochester. Rochester, N.Y. 1962.

Ramo, Dr. Simon, "The Scientific Challenge of the New Age,"

Address to 65th Annual Congress of American Industry, New York. December 7, 1960.

Sayre, Wallace, "Scientists and American Science Policy," Address to AAAS, New York. December 27, 1960.

Seaborg, Glenn T., "Freedom and the Scientific Society—The Third Revolution," Williamsburg, Va. May 26, 1962.

Seaborg, Glenn T., "The Third Revolution," George Washington University, Washington, D.C. June 6, 1962.

Seaborg, Glenn T., "Nuclear Science and the Strategies for Peace," Los Angeles World Affairs Council. October 9, 1962.

Seaborg, Glenn T., "Toward an Open Scientific Community," George Washington University, Washington, D.C., October 16, 1962.

Seaborg, Glenn T., "91st Convocation," University of the State of New York, New York, 1962.

Snow, Charles P., "The Moral Un-Neutrality of Science," Annual Meeting of AAAS, New York. December 27, 1960.

Teller, Edward, "Science and Politics," Kenyon College. Gambier, Ohio. October 27, 1961.

Warren, Chief Justice Earl, "75th Anniversary," Georgia Institute of Technology, Atlanta, Ga. February 12, 1963.

## IV. NEWSPAPERS AND EDITORIALS

Calder, Nigel, "Science Notebook," *New Statesman,* London. May 4, 1962.

Colburn, Robert, "In Our Opinion," *International Science and Technology*. May, 1962.

Cousins, Norman, "A Thin But Important Opening," *Saturday Review*. March 2, 1963.

Editors of *Fortune*. "Office of Hairbrained Ideas," *Fortune*. February, 1961.

Editors of *Science,* "Science and Foreign Affairs," *Science*. October 12, 1962.

Editors of the *New York Times,* "Physicist G. F. Tape Picked as New Member of A.E.C.," *New York Times*. March 21, 1963.

Editors of *Sane World,* "Test Ban Treaty Under Partisan Attack," *Sane World*. March 1, 1963.

Finney, John, "AEC Prize Going to Oppenheimer," *New York Times.* April 5, 1963.

Fischer, John, "A Scientific Formula for Disarmament," *Harper's.* January, 1963.

Hoppe, Art, "Chicken Little vs. Men of Science," *San Francisco Chronicle.* May 2, 1962.

Krock, Arthur, "Tiger in a Gilded Cage," *Philadelphia Bulletin.* March 8, 1963.

Krock, Arthur, "Bundy Article and the Princeton Alumni," *New York Times News Service.* March 12, 1963.

Laurence, William, "Aftereffects of U.S. Nuclear Explosion," *New York Times.* September 16, 1962.

Lovell, Sir Bernard, "American Roulette 500 Miles Up," *The Observer,* London. May 6, 1962.

Middleton, Drew, "Sweden Asks for Scientific Unit to Prepare Treaty to Bar Tests," *New York Times.* November 29, 1962.

Reston, James, "Inner Conflict," *New York Times News Service.* March 23, 1963.

Reston, James, "The Man on the Moon and the Man on the Dole," *New York Times.* April 5, 1963.

Singer, S. Fred, "Space Gambling? No!," *The Observer,* London. June 3, 1962.

Sullivan, Walter, "Radiation Belt Made by H-Bomb Produces Audible Hiss," *New York Times.* October 14, 1962.

## V. REPORTS, PAMPHLETS, TV PROGRAMS AND STATEMENTS

American Academy of Political and Social Science. "Perspectives on Government in Science," *Annals.* January, 1960. (Entire issue.)

Bethe, Hans, "Science." An interview, Center for the Study of Democratic Institutions, Pasadena, Calif. 1962.

Center for the Study of Democratic Institutions (report), "Science, Scientists and Politics," Santa Barbara, Calif. 1963.

Commoner, Barry et al., "Science and Human Welfare." Report to AAAS. July 8, 1960.

Council for Abolishing War. "A Livable World Free from War," 1963 Action Program, Washington, D.C. (Report.)

Douglas, William O., "Freedom of the Mind." American Library Association, New York. 1962. (Pamphlet.)

Federation of American Scientists. Civil Defense Shelters Statement. November, 1961.

"Science and Human Survival." AAAS Committee Report. July 8, 1960.

"Science in the Promotion of Human Welfare." AAAS Committee Report. December 29, 1961.

Sevareid, Eric, et al., "The Great Challenge—Where Is Science Taking Us." CBS-TV network program. February 10, 1963.

Sevareid, Eric, et al., "The Silent Spring of Rachel Carson." CBS Reports. (Network TV documentary.) April 3, 1963.

Space Science Board. "A Review of Space Research." N.A.S. Report. Washington, D.C. January 5, 1963.

Stover, Carl, "The Government of Science." Center for the Study of Democratic Institutions. Santa Barbara, Calif. 1962.

Szent-Gyorgi, Albert, "Scientists' Statement to Postpone All High Altitude Nuclear Tests." National Committee for SANE Nuclear Policy. New York. May 23, 1962.

## VI. U.S. GOVERNMENT PUBLICATIONS

U.S. Government Printing Office, *In the Matter of J. Robert Oppenheimer,* Transcript of Hearings before Personnel Security Board. Washington, D.C., 1954.

House Subcommittee Report, *"Organization and Administration of Military R&D Programs.* Report, U.S. House of Representatives, Rep. Walter Riehlman, Chairman. June 8–24, 1954.

National Science Foundation, *Organization of the Federal Government for Science Activities.* Office of Special Studies Report. Washington. 1956.

U.S. Senate Preparedness Investigating Subcommittee of the Committee on Armed Services, Hearings, *Inquiry Into Satellites and Missile Programs.* 85th Congress, 1st and 2nd, Sessions, 1957–58.

*NACA Resolution on the Subject of Spaceflight,* adopted January 16, 1958, in the U.S. House of Representatives, Select Committee on Astronautics and Space Exploration. *Committee Report,* No. 1758. 85th Congress, 2nd Session, May 21, 1958.

U.S. Senate, Special Committee on Space and Astronautics, Compilation of Materials on Space and Astronautics, No. 1, *National Space Establishment.* 85th Congress, 2nd Session, March 27, 1958.

U.S. House of Representatives, Select Committee on Astronautics and Space Exploration, Hearings on H.R. 11881. 85th Congress, 2nd Session, 1958.

U.S. Senate Special Committee on Space and Astronautics, Hearings on S. 3609. 85th Congress, 2nd Session, 1958.

U.S. Senate Foreign Relations Committee. *"Possible Non-Military Scientific Developments and Their Potential Impact on Foreign Policy Problems of the United States.* Stanford Research Institute, No. 2. September, 1959.

*Department of State Bulletin.* "The Role of Science in Foreign Policy Planning," by Wallace Brode. February 22, 1960. Vol. XLII.

*Department of State Bulletin.* "Science and Foreign Affairs," by George B. Kistiakowsky. February 22, 1960. Vol. XLII.

*Department of State Bulletin.* "National and International Science," by Wallace R. Brode. May 9, 1960. Vol. XIII.

*Scientific Progress, the Universities and the Federal Government.* PSAC Report to White House, Glenn Seaborg, Chairman. Superintendent of Documents, Washington, D.C. November 15, 1960.

U.S. Senate Subcommittee on National Policy Machinery of Senate Government Operations Committee, *Organizing for National Security,* Washington, D.C. August, 1961.

U.S. National Science Foundation. *Investing in Scientific Progress, 1961–1970.* Washington, D.C. 1961.

*Independent Offices Appropriations for 1963.* [Testimony of Dr. Jerome Wiesner.] Hearings Before a Subcommittee of the Committee on Appropriations, U.S. House of Representatives, 87th Congress, July 9, 1962.

*Statement* of Dr. Jerome Wiesner before the Military Operations Subcommittee of the House Committee on Government Operations on Matters Pertaining to Science Organization et al., July, 1962.

*Nomination of Dr. Jerome Wiesner to Be Director, Office of Science and Technology.* Hearing before Committee on Labor and Public Welfare, U.S. Senate, 87th Congress, 2nd Session, July 17, 1962.

*Statement* of Dr. Wiesner to Senate Subcommittee on Reorganization and International Organizations. September 12, 1962.

## VII. LETTERS TO THE AUTHOR

*David Z. Beckler* (for Jerome Wiesner), October 26, 1962. *Harold Brown,* November 13, 1962. *Harrison Brown,* November 20, 1962. *Hugh Dryden,* December 6, 1962. *Freeman Dyson,* November 18, 1962. *Loren Eiseley,* January 9, 1963. *Bernard Feld,* December 3, 1962. *Allan Forbes* (for Leo Szilard), December 31, 1962. *David Inglis,* November 30, 1962. *James R. Killian,* November 20, 1962. *Linus Pauling,* November 27, 1962. *Glenn Seaborg,* November 10, 1962. *Harold Urey,* December 3, 1962. *James Warwick,* January 23, 1963. *Herbert York,* November 8, 1962.

# Appendix A
# Chronological Growth of Science
# in the U.S. Government—
# Significant Milestones

| Date | Event |
|------|-------|
| 1790 | Establishment of the U.S. Patent Office; inauguration of decennial census and development of a uniform system of weights and measures. |
| 1807 | U.S. Coastal Survey established. |
| 1832 | First grant for experimental research to the Franklin Institute for investigation of explosions in steam boilers. |
| 1836 | First distribution of seeds to farmers by the Comissioner of Patents. |
| 1837 | First Federal regulatory agency—Steamboat Inspection Service. |
| 1846 | Smithsonian Institution founded. |
| 1862 | Establishment of the Department of Agriculture and passage of the Morrill Act. |
| 1863 | National Academy of Sciences chartered. |
| 1901 | National Bureau of Standards established. |
| 1903 | Departments of Commerce and Labor established (mainly to conduct research of industrial and labor problems). |
| 1915 | National Advisory Committee on Aeronautics formed. |
| 1942 | Office of Scientific Research and Development established. |
| 1946 | Atomic Energy Commission and Office of Naval Research established. |
| 1950 | National Science Foundation established. |
| 1952 | Chief of Research and Development in the Office of the Chief of Staff, U.S. Army, established. |

| Date | Event |
|------|-------|
| 1957 | Department of Defense reorganized, setting up Director of Research and Engineering; Special Assistant to President for Science and Technology appointed, and President's Science Advisory Committee created. |
| 1958 | Birth of the National Aeronautics and Space Administration, and passage of the National Defense Education Act. |
| 1959 | Federal Council on Science and Technology established. |
| 1960 | Assistant Secretary for R&D in each service department established in the Department of Defense. |
| 1962 | Incorporation of PSAC into the White House organization, and elevation of Chairman to status of full-time science adviser. |
| 1963 | Influence of scientists led political leaders to sign and approve nuclear test-ban treaty. |

# Appendix B

# Glossary of Abbreviations
# of U.S. Governmental and Professional
# Scientific Organizations

**AAAS**—American Association for the Advancement of Science.
**AEC**—Atomic Energy Commission.
**AIAA**—American Institute of Aeronautics and Astronautics.
**AIBS**—American Institute of Biological Sciences.
**ARPA**—Advanced Research Projects Agency.
**ARS**—American Rocket Society.
**ASTIA**—Armed Forces Technical Information Agency.
**BAS**—Bulletin of the Atomic Scientists.
**COSPAR**—Special Committee on Space Research (ICSU).
**COSWA**—Conference on Science and World Affairs (Pugwash).
**DOD**—Department of Defense.
**FAS**—Federation of American Scientists.
**FCST**—Federal Council on Science and Technology.
**GAC**—General Advisory Committee.
**HEW**—Health, Education and Welfare (Department).
**ICSU**—International Council of Scientific Unions.
**IGY**—International Geophysical Year.
**NACA**—National Advisory Committee on Aeronautics.
**NAS**—National Academy of Sciences.
**NASA**—National Aeronautics and Space Administration.
**NASC**—National Aeronautics and Space Council.
**NDEA**—National Defense Education Act.
**NRC**—National Research Council.
**NSF**—National Science Foundation.
**NSIA**—National Security Industrial Association.

**OE**—Office of Education (HEW).
**ONR**—Office of Naval Research.
**OSRD**—Office of Scientific Research and Development.
**OST**—Office of Science and Technology.
**PSAC**—President's Science Advisory Committee.
**RAND**—Research and Development Corp.
**R&D**—Research and Development.
**SCAW**—Szilard Council for Abolishing War.
**SSB**—Space Science Board (NAS).
**STL**—Space Technology Laboratories.

## Appendix C

# COMMITTEE ON NATIONAL RESOURCES, NATIONAL ACADEMY OF SCIENCES: National Resources: A Summary Report to the President of the U.S.A.[1]

Perhaps the most critical and most often ignored resource is man's total environment. Increasing awareness of the importance of understanding the balances of nature is reflected in the gradual development of interest in ecological studies. The study of the interaction of all biologic species, among themselves and with the inanimate forces of nature, requires coordination of the contributions of all the sciences, natural and social.

The wisdom of examining environment in the totality of its interaction with man becomes increasingly apparent in view of the rapidity of environmental change in our country. We live in a period of social and technological revolution, in which man's ability to manipulate the processes of nature for his own economic and social purposes is increasing at a rate which his forebears would find frightening.

Man is altering the balance of a relatively stable system by his pollution of the atmosphere with smoke, fumes, and particles from fossil fuels, industrial chemicals, and radioactive material; by his alteration of the energy and water balance at the earth's surface by deforestation, afforestation, cultivation of land, shading, mulching,

[1] NAS Publication No. 1,000, 1963.

281

over-grazing grasslands, reduction of evapotranspiration, irrigation, drainage of large swamp lands, and the building of cities and highways; by his clearing forests and alterations of plant surface cover, changing the reflectivity of the earth's surface and soil structures; by his land-filling, construction of buildings and seawalls, and pollution, bringing about radical changes in the ecology of estuarine areas; by the changes he effects in the biologic balance and the physical relocation of water basins through the erection of dams and channel works; and by the increasing quantities of carbon dioxide an industrial society releases to the atmosphere.

There is a continuing worldwide movement of population to the cities. The patterns of society are being rapidly rearranged, and new sets of aspirations, new evaluations of what constitutes a resource, and new requirements in both type and quantity of resources are resulting.

The effects on man himself of the changes he has wrought in the balance of great natural forces and in the new microenvironment which he has created are but dimly perceived and not at all well understood. The following examples suggested by observable changes in environment illustrate questions for which answers should be sought through research.

*Environmental Health and Disease.* Little is known of the short-term or long-term effects on man's health and productivity of the great variety of air and water pollutants, in terms of his ability to adapt, to build up resistance over what periods of time, and to tolerate what levels of toxicity. Neurological disorders and physiological reactions have been traced to some of these pollutants.

*Geographic and Time Distribution of Disease.* Diseases such as cancer and heart disease are in some way environmentally linked, but the mechanisms of linkage are not now known. As various environments have become more industrialized they have shown a rise in certain types of cancer, a drop in others.

*The Environment and Biological Functioning.* Man, after tens of thousands of years of very slow, very gradual change in environment, has in the past few hundred years made radical and abrupt changes to which he has to adjust more rapidly than ever before. Evidence indicates significant physiological and psychological reactions to such changes, but neither the causes nor the short- or long-range results are clear. Among the changed regimes which produce these physical and mental effects, still to be precisely identified and measured, are: the provision of artificial climates for increasing numbers of our population, changes in the light-dark cycles, changes in temperature and humidity, and increase in ambient noise levels.

There is a host of components of the physical atmosphere that are bioclimatic in nature, which affect, or in some cases are presumed to affect, human biology. Those known to have such effects include motion of air, atmospheric pressure fluctuations, the chemical composition of air, ionizing radiations, and atmospheric electricity. In the "presumed-effects" group are radio waves, long-wave radiation, space charges, electrostatic fields, and variations in atmospheric pressures.

*Climatic Modifications.* Man has worked assiduously to control or change natural phenomena for his benefit. He has tried particularly to influence weather and climate by modification of the atmosphere. There has been a long history of efforts to induce precipitation artificially, to cause the dissipation of cloud cover, and to reduce the violence of storms.

Many of the questions relating to the artificial induction of rain are far from settled; there is no solid basis at present either for rejection or for optimism. In cloud dissipation, it has been demonstrated that the seeding technique used for inducing precipitation could be used to cut holes in clouds as well, but this effect has not proved particularly practical yet.

Seeding of hurricanes, extratropical cyclones, and thunderstorms to dissipate or release their effects has been tried only on a limited scale, and as yet without significant results. Understanding of the development and movement of such disturbances is so imperfect that it is doubtful that a significant, man-induced influence could now be recognized. Any program to control storms must await the development of understanding of the natural processes involved.

In summary, it is apparent that man must concern himself with a variety of changes in the environment, both those caused by human beings and those reflecting man's responses. Some are good; some may be very harmful. That we often do not have any clear-cut idea of their impact on man, or of man's response, is cause for concern. It would seem unwise to continue to tamper with environment without, concurrently, striving to determine the real and lasting effects of our actions.

# Index

# Donald W. Cox

is a noted free-lance lecturer who has won a wide following
with his keen interpretations of past, present, and future astro-
nautical events. He is the author of a half-dozen books on
various aspects of space science, including the critically ac-
claimed *The Space Race*. This leading Space Age educator was
formerly associated with the National Aeronautics and Space
Administration, where he pioneered the nation's first traveling
space science demonstration unit in schools and colleges; Project
*Vanguard,* America's first artificial earth satellite program;
New York University, the Air Command and Staff College, the
University of Florida, and the University of Alabama, where he
held responsible staff positions.